Along the Lines...

Selected writings from Ross-shire

Ross-shire Writers

Published by:
Ross shire Writers,
'Arnish',
9 Academy Crescent,
Dingwall
IV15 9LW

Printed by Dingwall Printers

Front Cover Photo: ©Vivien-Christine
Back Cover Photo: ©Reg Holder

Acknowledgements

Ross-shire Writers wish to express their appreciation of support from
WEA and funding from:

ISBN 978-0-9554876-0-6

CONTENTS

FOREWORD

Ross-shire Writers is a vibrant group of aspiring writers meeting regularly in Dingwall. It grew from an original creative writing class tutored by Cynthia Rogerson some six years ago under the auspices of the Workers' Educational Association to which it remains affiliated.

In September 2003 the group was formalised as Ross-shire Writers. It draws its members from a wide geographical area and from different backgrounds all of which adds richness and diversity to their writing.

Along the Lines... is their second production, the first being an in-house anthology in 2005, circulated to family and friends. Some members have been published and have won competitions; for others this is the first opportunity to present their work to the public. They have also broadcast on hospital radio at Raigmore and Moray Firth Radio

The group acknowledges and is grateful to the Highland Council and Highland Year of Culture 2007 for their financial assistance and support in producing this book.

They hope that you will enjoy the selection of stories and poems that follow.

MESSAGE
Heather Macleod

The wind brought it, obviously.
Plummetting with gannets,
caught up
in the slip stream of whoopers
skeining the machair,
blown across bog.

You could hear its bat-fluttering
through the depths of creation,
and the howl of it to an opal moon.
It came on the whispers of Inuits,
in the irreversible plipping
of melting ice.
You could smell it even,
in ancient spawning of salmon.
Or tune into warm wavelengths,
voraciously compressed,
and hear the panic.
It was mapped out in mangrove-maze,
and in the trogon's fluted flight
to the last untouched branch.
Shards of it gathered in dead shells of seabirds.
The basking shark mouthed it as it moved north,
the common frog croaked its chorus.
It was etched in salt
on dense pelts of polar bear,
and sealed with an ape's glazed eye.
It was addressed to a hedonistic race
heading for extinction.
But those of that race didn't hear, they couldn't see.
They had lost all sense.
And so it blew on,
unheeded.

THE RICHEST MAN IN THE DISTRICT
Reg Holder

Mr Chanubai Babu, a man of habit, always rose early and after completing his morning puja took a brief walk in the garden before it was time for breakfast. This was usually light, perhaps an idli with curds or sometimes fruit from the orchard such as a mango or papaya. Advancing into middle age, weight was becoming a problem and he had to take care not to eat too much these days. He preferred to think that he was on the right side of portly and, to reflect his position as the owner of a large tea estate, he did need to show a certain amount of girth. The estate was situated in the hills above Cochin and apart from tea had orchards of mangos, guavas and other fruit. He was well off by all accounts and in his opinion must be the district's richest man.

When his father died he had taken over the estate and under his stewardship it had been carefully brought into a modern and profitable condition. He was therefore accorded a great deal of respect, especially by those estate workers and families who depended on him for their very existence. In the tradition of his family Mr Babu accepted that he had a duty to care for them, not only to provide labour for the estate but also in keeping with a paternal figure of substance.

On this day Mr Babu had woken with a faint air of disquiet, one of those vague feelings that ripple through one's stomach and on up into the chest. He couldn't place a finger on it for he felt quite well, and soon dismissed his apprehension, putting it down to the worry of the forthcoming tea sales. The market was not good this year and much of the tea earmarked for regular customers had not yet been taken up.

Finishing his breakfast and looking in on his wife to say good morning he went to his office to continue his routine. Rajul, his clerk, stood at his side handing him the various papers and memos that required attention. Many were petitions from the poor of the area and also some from the better off, looking for placements for their sons, asking him to use his influence in gaining them. Rajul Srinagar, MBA, issued from the college in Cochin, was of course the filter for all this and nothing reached his Master's attention except through him. Rajul had great influence and was thus able to ensure that his own finances were supplemented to a reasonable extent, though he had to be careful not to overdo things.

Paperwork finished, Mr Babu picked up the telephone to make a few calls. The first was to the State Minister of Trade to solicit his support in the matter of a dispute with a neighbouring estate and to discuss the state of the market. Another call was to the district magistrate who was holding court that morning. One of his garden foremen was appearing before him on charges of beating his wife. The man of course deserved punishment but Mr Babu needed him on the estate and a spell in prison would serve no purpose.

Yes, overall he was a contented man and his fortunes were generally prospering despite the poor prices at the moment. His sons were doing well in college and he looked forward to one of them taking over and affording him a comfortable retirement.

Today he decided that he would look at his gardens on foot, walking first through the orchards and then to the lower end of the estate where his driver would pick him up to take him home for lunch. Waddling down the pathway at the back of the house through the mango trees he looked up at the sky and saw the clouds gathering, huge cumulo-nimbus. This was unusual for the time of year and somehow full of foreboding. He decided to shorten his inspection and cut down by the hedge bordering a field where he kept his cows. He did not care for the buffalo milk that was prevalent in the area and over the years he had carefully built up his herd.

Entering the first garden his heart lifted. The sight of the neat bushes in orderly rows with the women in colourful saris tending to their work always filled him with pleasure. He went on down the hill and as he passed they averted their eyes and stopped their chattering. The path now took him past the forest edge and a number of small huts dotted in the trees. Not all the workers lived in the labour lines and many who had finished their working lives liked to move there and still be near to their families.

The air was now stifling. The clouds, towering into the sky and blackening by the minute, suddenly opened to release torrential sheets of rain. Running to the nearest hut he knocked urgently, requesting permission to enter. In the gloom he made out an old man sitting quietly on his own, tending to his devotions, his beads moving silently through his hands. Mr Babu removed his shoes and sat quietly, waiting patiently for him to finish. The elderly, of whatever station in life, had to be treated with respect and Mr Babu always observed the ways of his people.

Finishing his prayers, the old man spoke softly in the gloom, "I see you, Sahib, welcome to my house." Reaching over he courteously poured out a glass of milk and drew a small roti from the chatty tin that his granddaughter brought him every day. It was often filled with vegetables that the family grew in the small patch by their hut. "My needs, Sahib, are as you can see, simple, and my devotions also sustain me through the day."

The rain continued unabated making it difficult to hear the old man but Mr Babu did not take time into account and sat enthralled in the presence of a good man, conversing with him on the spiritual essentials of life. Eventually, however, the rain stopped and Mr Babu reluctantly rose to take his leave, making a note to return at the first opportunity. He was heartened now and his earlier disquiet gone.

"Chello! I must go, old sir, and my respects to you until the time that I may return."

"Farewell, Sahib," said the old man, his eyes misting and his hands resuming his beads. "Farewell. I shall not see you again, for here tonight the richest man will die."

Mr Babu left, his mind disturbed. He was certainly not ready to accept his fate so soon. He hurried home and quickly phoned the doctor who had his clinic in the small town some miles away. He knew him well for they were friends and he often came to sit on the veranda and sip sundowners while they caught up on the happenings of the district.

"Come, Doctor Sahib, you must come at once for I have disturbing news which I shall explain when you arrive."

The doctor, much alarmed, quickly saw the remaining patients in the clinic and hurried over, bag in hand, stethoscope in his top pocket. Examining Mr Babu he could find nothing physically wrong with him, expect for his obvious agitation.

"I'll stay the night with you," he said, "and if the worst should happen I shall be on hand."

"Thank you, dear friend," said Mr Babu. "After we have eaten I shall try to sleep and will say goodbye to you before then. If fate should arrive to claim me then so be it." He did not tell his wife and he was careful to say his goodnight in such a way so as not to alarm her. Retiring to an easy chair alongside the doctor he fell into an uneasy doze and waited.

Dawn arrived, mist rising up from the valley, the sun breaking through, its early warmth dissipating the swirling tendrils and drying out the dew-speckled grass. Opening his eyes Mr Babu eased his stiffened limbs and slowly rose from the chair and looked across to the doctor, gently snoring. Although much relieved that the old man's prediction had not come to pass, the uneasy hours had raised many disturbing questions and he decided that very day, he must sit with him again for he had much to learn.

Hearing voices he looked up towards the gardens. There he saw a procession slowly wending its way along the path, the women weeping, the men silent, carrying their sad cargo to the funeral pyre. Summoning Rajul, he sent him to enquire as to who had died.

"He was an old man, Sahib, one of those who lived in the forest, not an important man. They tell me he had lived many years and that his time had come. They are sad of course, Sahib."

Mr Chanubai Babu was humbled.

FRIENDS
Caroline Robinson

The blind man knew it was the post van because of its leaky silencer and the squealing slip of its fan-belt. By the time Hugo the Post had carried the heavy packages up to the open door, Niall had clanked the kettle back on the hob and set out the teapot and mugs.

"Tis yerself, Hugo, the very man I prayed would come to help me with my predicament. Come away in and have a cup. See, the kettle is singing for you."

"How are you today Niall? I have these three thick envelopes here and a card from Florida from your Jessie. My, now wouldn't that be grand? I can feel the heat from the picture on the front."

The two men sat sipping tea as Hugo opened the mail and read out his friend's news: two rejected manuscripts, one possible acceptance with a list of amendments required and the postcard from Niall's daughter.

"The wummin, where I'm doing the readings, wants me to *spruce up*. Bloody cheek, but there you have it." Niall stared unseeing into the distance. His friend not having understood asked him to repeat slower, so he could follow his lips.

Hugo, forgetting, nodded in understanding. "We'll hit the town, get you new stuff, visit the barbers. Dinnae fash yerself. Nae problem, but I have a favour to tak' in exchange."

The deaf postie took from his pocket a Jew's harp, placed it in his mouth and plucked a haunting melody, moving his jaw to oscillate the notes.

Niall leant back in his chair and saw the river and lochs, the mountain range and gorge, the soaring, hesitant flight of the sea eagle.

Hugo laid the harp down on the dirty, deal table and looked to the poet, awaiting his comment.

After a while Niall said, "I went the walk along the Struie when you played. It had all the details, the colours, the sounds, the fresh wind. I could even smell the peats stacked to dry. It was a grand journey you took me on."

Hugo replied, "When you had me type out your *Ode to Anchellach*, I sat down and made that up as I reread it through, following your words with my harp clamped a'tween my jaws. I heard the sounds in my head from the pictures you drew with your words. What would we be, God, where would we be, if with a heart full of hate and a mind twisted wi' spite we hadn't made that bomb that melted your eyes and pierced my ear drums? Would we be deid? Would we be prisoners or sodgers fighting fer a cause we had no mind fer?"

The blind man replenished their cups with a wee dram of malt, held his cup aloft and pronounced, "Only the Devil knows, but this I know fu' well, we'd still be friends."

ANGEL IN A CORNER
L. A. Hollywood

Angel, you stand in a corner
of the forgotten graveyard,
no longer in sight.
Once fine marble, you've lost your shine,
wings covered by rambling roses,
your halo a nest for a robin,
nose broken off by a falling branch
long ago.
With one hand,
you still blow your trumpet,
pointing it to the heavens.
No one's listening.
Your fingers from the other hand
lost, so that it looks like a fist
Raised in anger.

JELLY BABIES
Henriette A.O. Stewart

Soft whispering in his ear, quietly calling his name. One moment, right beside him, the next, far away. Inquisitive at first but growing more and more urgent until it sounds panicked and frightened. Then it stops. And there is only silence again. He feels the loneliness of unsound rush in.

No! Don't go. Say my name again. Say it out loud.

(Nothing).

Sunlight. He was awake. He sat up and threw the quilt off. It slid down onto the white linoleum floor with a tired whisper. His t-shirt clung to his sweaty chest and back.

This room he knew. Over there was the toilet and bathroom, and toothbrush. In that chest of drawers were clothes for him to put on. Out that window you could look into the garden which had benches and flowers and bushes and a tall wall around it. And through that door would come doctors and nurses and other kinds of people who wanted to help him get better. Help him remember.

The door opened.

"Ah, you are awake already. How are you feeling today?" The male nurse went over to the little bedside table and filled up the empty glass from the water jug.

"Here, you look thirsty," he said holding out the glass, but the young man on the bed shook his head.

"I think you should shower before you get dressed," the nurse said, putting the glass down. "I'll find something nice and smart for you to wear."

The nurse crossed the room to the chest of drawers. "You are meeting Mrs Meyers today; she is very clever, so you'll want to dress to impress." He pulled out jeans, shirt, t-shirt, pants and socks, and laid them in a neat pile on top of the dresser.

The young man's eyes never left the nurse as he bustled round the room. The sweat in his hair was making his scalp itch but he ignored it. Finally the nurse left. The young man jumped off the bed and went the bathroom where he turned on the cold water tap and drank from it with big greedy gulps.

Mrs Meyers was already seated when the young man came into the room.

"Take a seat," she said gesturing towards the armchair opposite her own. She looked like a schoolteacher with her greying hair and delicate navy-blue cardigan.

As he sat down in the armchair, he noticed the bag of jelly babies lying unopened on the table between them.

"Would you like a jelly baby?" Mrs Meyers asked. He nodded. She took the bag, opened it and held the open end out towards him.

Colourful and sugar-dusted, the jelly babies lay in the bag presenting him with their heads and feet. He picked a yellow one and put it in his mouth. The sugar melted instantly in his mouth and he sighed at the sweet rush which almost brought tears to his eyes. Slowly he let his tongue explore the jelly baby's face and body before crushing it to the roof of his mouth. The jelly baby's hardened coating cracked and the young man's mind was suddenly filled with the flavour of yellow.

The sun is beating down on the back of his head, and the glossy slats of the bench he is sitting on are sticking to his bare legs. He is looking down a stony beach, towards the water's edge. Two boys are throwing stones into the water, and their shouts and laughter are entrancing him like a siren's song.

Beside him, on the bench, sits an old lady. Her hands are shaking slightly as they twist and wring a lace-edged handkerchief. She turns and leans her head close to his and says, "Don't hate the sea."

The young man swallowed the jelly baby and looked at Mrs Meyers across the table. She was smiling.

"You had a memory just now, didn't you?"

He nodded.

"Would you like another one?" she asked.

He picked a green jelly baby and put it in his mouth.

Faster, faster; he must not get caught. No time to look behind him. The grass a green blur under his bare feet, his breath noisy gasps in his ears.

A strong hand grabs the back of his shirt and brings him to the ground. The man is breathing heavily too. Angry eyes, stern voice.

"You ungrateful brat, we're not keeping you a minute longer."

I didn't mean to. Please Mr Gillespie, don't send me away. I'm sorry, please, please. He can't say the words out loud. Suffocating regret constricts his throat. Hot tears wipe out the edges of the man.

Mrs Meyers held out a box of tissues. The young man pulled one out, wiped his eyes and blew his nose.

"You don't like the green ones much I take it?"

The young man looked at her. Her expression was kind but unemotional. He looked out the window to avoid her eyes.

"How about another one?" she asked.

The young man picked up the bag and looked into it, taking his time, choosing carefully. Finally he pulled out a white one and put it in his mouth.

Everything is obscured by some kind of fog, but he is sure he is still inside the house. It doesn't seem dark, it isn't night and he isn't in his bed, but on the floor.

He tries to get up but his head seems too heavy to lift. It must be a dream. He stops trying to get up and lies back down.

The floorboards feel hot on his cheek. It feels good but something is wrong. Wrong.

A knock on the door brought him back.

"Come in," called Mrs Meyers. It was the tea lady with her trolley. The young man shook his head. He didn't feel like drinking something hot.

Mrs Meyers returned to her seat, gingerly holding a china cup in one hand and a saucer in the other. The steam rose from her cup like smoke from a dying fire. The young man looked at the bag of jelly babies on the table. Some had tumbled out, along with a patch of fine sugar dust.

"Feel free," Mrs Meyers said. The young man put his hand into the bag and pulled out a jelly baby. It was orange.

"Don't listen to the other children, don't talk to them. Only your teacher." The old woman across the rickety dining table is his granny; he recognises the funny brown spots on her hands.

"Eat up now, eat up," she says. He looks at the food in the bowl in front of him. Cornflakes. He usually likes that but he doesn't feel hungry at all. He knows it isn't a school day today; it is the middle of the Easter holidays, but granny will be cross if he tells her. Beside him on the table lies a small pile of Christmas cards he has to post on his way to school.

The young man leant back in the chair and crossed his arms. This was an annoying memory, but it filled a space where there had been nothing.

Mrs Meyers put her teacup on the table with a gentle clink. "You are welcome to tell me what you are thinking, at any time."

The young man shook his head and shrugged his shoulders.

For a few minutes they just sat there, looking at the bag of jelly babies and out the window, like strangers at a bus stop, having nothing in common but waiting for the same thing.

On the table, near the opening of the bag, the young man could see a black jelly baby nestled between two yellow ones. He picked it up. The fine white sugar made its blackness look grey, but when he held it up to the light of the window, it became purple. He wanted to return it to the bag, but he was curious. Very slowly he put it into his mouth.

Big dark boulder-like clouds roll across the sky and the waves are growing more and more restless and violent, making the little rowing boat jump and dive. He has lost his oars a long time ago.

The howling wind is penetrating his sodden clothes and stinging his skin.

He closes his eyes, and feels closer than ever to the edge of madness. This must be how they felt their last hours and minutes before the sea swallowed them up, leaving him orphaned. He is closer to them than ever before, only his hands are refusing to let go of the sides of the boat.

It had grown dark but slowly the darkness didn't seem so dark after all.

"I didn't drown."

For a moment the young man wasn't sure who had spoken. The voice was soft but slightly hoarse, like it hadn't been used for a long time. It was his own.

"You were found wandering on the beach," Mrs Meyers said. "Can you remember any thing else?"

The young man looked at the bag of jelly-babies. He did remember some things now. His parents had died, drowned, when he was a boy and his grandmother had taken care of him. She had been very strict, and hadn't allowed him to play with other children. Her memory became poor and grew worse, soon getting so bad she would sometimes forget who he was. One day she'd left something on the cooker and gone to nap on her bed, and he'd been rescued from the burning house out the first floor window, but his grandmother hadn't survived. He had been taken into care and shunted from foster home to foster home until he was finally old enough to live by himself. The first money he received was earmarked for furniture for his bed-sit, but he'd spent it on a rowing boat and waited for really bad weather.

The young man was quiet for a long time.

Mrs Meyers broke the silence.

"Would you like another jelly baby?"

He'd had all the colours, hadn't he? He picked up the bag and looked into it. No, there was still red left to try. He fished out a red one, and put it in his mouth, doubting it would bring him anything happy.

19

He knows he is in trouble. There is a dent in the car door, an exact concave match to the pillar beside the car. The pillar has bits of red paint on it.

He closes the car door, but it is no use, his mum would have heard the crunch. Time is standing still while he wishes a thousand times that it hadn't happened.

"Henry Taylor," shouts his mum, her face contorted in anger, his name echoing through the parking level.

The young man took a sharp intake of breath. Mrs Meyers looked at him attentively.

"Yes?" she said, "Did that give you a memory?"

The expression in the young man's eyes were fearful for a moment, then he relaxed and looked out of the window. Out there, a gull flew by, unhurried and carefree.

"No," he answered. "Nothing."

DOWN WATER
Susan Szymborski

I'm across the river from you,
Down water.
I can see you through the spray
Amongst the trees and rocks.

I don't know how I got here,
Swept by the current
But worse,
I don't know if I can get back:
The water might sweep me away
And you mayn't reach to help.

PLANTS SHE LOVED
Christina Macdonald

Eliza was seated outside the back door of the cottage. The sun had been up for a few hours and the south-facing garden was still and warm. When a slight breeze lifted, a drift of perfume from the honeysuckle floated in the air and she sighed with pleasure.

She had come outside for a brief respite from her daily chore to enjoy the fruits of her garden. Her life in the end cottage of Weavers' Row was like those of her neighbours – constantly filled with the clacking of the looms, hour after hour.

Theirs was a hard life in many ways, confined for hours to the dark interior of their humble cottages, but they also had precious time to themselves as they still worked from home.

Eliza's garden, like the others in the row, was a mass of colour. Weavers throughout history had taken a pride in their plants and her family, like many others, showed their flowers annually in the village competitions.

Auriculas were her favourite and a traditional weaver's flower. Many hours were spent cultivating these exotic plants with their striking colours of burgundy, purple or even palest silver-green ringed with white. They were grown in individual pots and displayed with immense pride on wooden shelves.

Her typical cottage garden was this morning ablaze with drifts of tall sapphire delphiniums and white Madonna lilies, growing in rich abandon, while bees hovered constantly, gathering their nectar before returning with their booty to the bee-hives by the far hawthorn hedge.

Vegetables grew among the flowers too, for every patch of ground was precious. Marigolds and radishes jostled with parsley and other herbs. Her garden provided all kinds of culinary delights and remedies for many ills.

She was content in this regular, contained existence of hers – simple, lowly maybe, but undisturbed by the pressures of the outside world, fast becoming industrialised.

Some of the folk she knew in the next village had abandoned their home looms, lured by the promise of more money in the nearby mills. Not her; she and those around her of the older generation had no will or desire to move.

She was content with her lot and her acceptance of the life she had been given was absolute. Her faith was simple and epitomised by the words in the sampler which hung above the inglenook:

Behind my Life the Weaver stands and works His wondrous will.
I leave it in His all-wise hands and trust His perfect skill.
Should mystery enshroud the plan and my short sight grow dim
I will not try the whole to see but leave each thread to Him.

THE MIDDLE AGE
Carol Fenelon

This softening of the flesh
is hard to bear.
This stretching of the skin
over brittle bones
leaving unploughed furrows
where hidden dreams
are buried.

This face does not
accord with the mind
whose fancies still fly
to an oasis within
this parched land of the
middle age,
being neither one thing
nor the other.

Primal fears and jealousy
when children overwhelm
with unbound energy,
raw and confident.
Time spins by in breathless fashion
reminding us now daily of
our heartbeats' mortality.

NATURAL DEATH ARRANGEMENTS
Valerie Weir

Dearest, when at the last you bury me

plant over my grave a white thorn tree

emblem of mother's clan Ogilvy

for hawthorn flourish of father's boyhood memory.

Please follow my instructions to the letter.

Plant primroses, such as mother and I gathered by Linhouse Water,

wood anemones, for Almondell's carpeted braes

where father and I walked on Sundays.

And oh my love, plant bluebells – sky mirrors in the oak-woods of Argyll

where you and I became enthralled awhile.

Ensure my coffin is environmentally friendly

designed to biodegrade quickly and cleanly.

And dearest, insist on a quiet ceremony

so all may hear that distant blackbird flute the litany.

DISCOVERING ART
Catriona Tawse

Nothing exciting ever happened in the West Highland hamlet where I grew up. Mothers kept clean houses and tidy well-fed children. Men folk ploughed and planted, baited lines and mended nets and saw to the welfare of their livestock, lambing, clipping and dipping. Each routine week ended on the Sabbath Day with whole families filing blackly into the watchful church on the hillside.

Depending on the alacrity of our morning rising we youngsters sauntered, trudged, or sprinted the mile to the school where we were kept in control by a woman small in stature but mighty in religious beliefs. Part of our education was to learn by heart vast chunks of the Psalms in Gaelic *and* how to precent them. I have only to hear the tune Kilmarnock and I am back in that orderly classroom with its dusmo-swept wooden floor where we stood 'toeing the line' lifting our voices to heaven under the stern direction of Miss MacDougall's fearsome pointer.

Back home we were expected to bring in peats, polish our boots, fetch milk from John the Crow (we had no cow ourselves) and of course do our homework which was all-important – reading to prepare, spellings to revise and two verses of Psalm 46 to learn. Only then were we free to do the things small boys do, kicking a ball up and down the road, clattering about two or three at a time on rusty old bicycles or annoying the girls playing houses and shoppies in the shelter of a fallen dyke. Their dolls' tea parties were a favourite target and many the sgleog I got from the back of my father's hand when my sister ran home to tell on us. There was a beached and derelict salmon coble into which we lads clambered to embark on daring voyages through dangerous waters in search of imagined foreign lands. We met many menacing cutlass-waving pirates on the way and my brother Archie being the smallest walked the plank every time.

Down the road was the little shop where our mothers bought the daily messages and the bodachs got their tobacco and the hard pandrops which helped the Sabbath sermon along. Most other things came from J.D.Williams catalogues or the occasional visit to the town. Maggie in the shop gloweringly handed over our Bulls-eyes and Beanos when we dared to appear before her beady-eyed scrutiny clutching our pocket-money pennies. It is hard to forget the day when we stood awkwardly in our little group and Sandy, son of John the Crow, suddenly and resoundingly broke wind. Well, out came Maggie from behind the counter and chased us smartly off the premises calling us dirty and filthy and disgusting, and threatening to tell our mothers. Behind the safe cover of a peat stack we fell about laughing and Sandy tried in vain to repeat his magnificent performance.

The annual arrival of the Board of Agriculture's huge bull always aroused much interested speculation but we never got the length of seeing him swing into action. We had the normal childish curiosity regarding the mysteries of reproduction and birth but these matters were skirted around or carefully avoided. So on the whole we were left to come to our own wildly inaccurate conclusions. Our lives were simple and innocent.

Death was different: death happened quite a lot and it came one early Spring day to Nancy MacArthur who had for most of her ninety-odd years inhabited the wee house across the field from ours. My mother, a kind and gentle soul, often chided me for suggesting that the old woman was a witch. Well, she did walk all bent over, she talked a lot to herself and had a succession of black cats – all obvious signs to me. As far as folk knew there was no surviving family, two world wars being largely responsible, so it came as a big surprise to learn that there were people moving in. It was rumoured that he was a great grand nephew or something complicated and word also got around that he was an *artist*. Shock waves spread among the worthy locals, and indignant whispers abounded. Pagan debauchery, corrupting the young, the work of Satan . . . and so on.

When Walter Kendall did arrive it was quite a let-down to find no sign of a cloven hoof or a forked tail although he did have a frightening shock of wild black hair and a beard to match . . . a retired pirate perhaps? The shabby cord trousers he wore were stained with paint and he smelled different too, not of sheep dip or tractor oil. His wife was a colourful character, long fair hair, shapeless knitted jerseys and flouncy skirts down to her feet. Her ear-rings were big gold hoops such as we had only ever seen in pictures of gipsy fortune tellers. A pirate *and* a gipsy? Things were looking up. Her name was Clarissa, another touch of glamour among the

Annies, Bellas and Cathys we were used to. We unanimously agreed that we would name the next mermaid we met on our ocean-going travels in her honour. Clarissa told people she was writing a book. That again raised a few eyebrows.

A natural mix of curiosity and Highland courtesy soon had the strangers welcomed into the community. Much to our amusement they made efforts to learn a bit of Gaelic. The everyday greeting of "Ciamar a tha sibh?" (How are you?) came out as "Come or a hash you." "Madainn mhath," (Good morning) Jimmy the Post would say encouragingly. "Ma ding var," Walter would happily reply, clearly delighted with his fluency. At ceilidhs Clarissa would jig and reel with her skirts flying and Walter had a song which became his party piece, it was about him being a poacher and went a bit like "It's mighty light on a shiny night on the sea-saw of the year." Or so we thought.

In time I moved up to the High School and bussed daily to town still raw and bashful even after a couple of years mixing with more worldly-minded contemporaries. Then along came Hogmanay, the most convivial night in the Scottish calendar, and my parents had agreed that I could wait up for the first time and take in the New Year. The peat fire was blazing. Cake, shortbread and bottles were laid out on the sideboard and I joined in the toast with a small glass of whisky well diluted with ginger beer. Then Walter arrived. He was tall and dark, so two out of three wasn't bad for a first-foot. By the look of him he had begun his celebrations well before the allotted hour. My father poured a dram. Walter reciprocated from his bottle as was the custom and it wasn't long before the poacher song was getting the works and he was begging my father for a tune on the button box which only appeared on rare occasions. Besides sharing the same name, Lachlan, my father and I were both shy folk. He was of course Lachie Mor and I was Lachie Beag, Walter managed Lackie but my mother was always Mrs MacLeod to him.

"Just you wait there, Lackie my friend," Walter began, rising unsteadily to his feet. "I have something for you in the house; I'll be back in a minute." Off he tottered into the night passing two of my father's cronies on their way in. They took their dram but refused with thanks my mother's offer of tea as they had just started on their rounds. They had scarcely reached the road end when Walter reappeared bearing his gift which he bestowed with drink-inspired benevolence.

I stood stock still and stared as I heard my mother say, "The boy, the boy," but Walter gave me such a nudge with his bony elbow I almost fell over.

"You're a big chap now, wee Lackie, I'm sure you know what's what," and he rewarded me with a full-on view of his offering which was a full-on view of Clarissa. Her head was flung back and she was laughing but there was no sign of any shapeless jersey, no flouncy skirt. I was not sure if she was even wearing the gold hoops – I was so taken aback, trying to look away and feeling fascinated at the same time.

"Off to bed with you, Lachie Beag," prompted my mother quite calmly as if we had naked ladies on display every day. I gladly fled.

Worse was to come the following afternoon. Clarissa appeared when I answered the door – with all her clothes on thankfully – and I felt my face turn as red as my hair. She seemed quite unconcerned and after a wee word and a thank you with my mother she gathered up the painting and bore it homewards. I found out later that this had become a yearly ritual. Walter would fetch some bizarre work of his art and Clarissa would discreetly retrieve it next day.

Over the years, I have served in the Merchant Navy with ships of my own to command and I have seen many strange sights but I will always remember discovering art in my quiet Highland home on that distant New Year night.

MISSING HER TRAIN
L. A. Hollywood

Maria runs down the steps on to the platform just as the train leaves. Dropping her case on a bench, she finds her phone to call the office, telling them she would be late for the meeting and to go ahead without her. Looking around she sees a man lying on a bench. He's looking at her, eyeing her up, scratching his face. He sits up, lifts a can to drink, then slings it onto the track. She makes a noise of disapproval. That's when it hits George – he knows her from somewhere long ago.

Maria is rummaging in her case. George looks at the case that goes with the tailor-made suit. So that's what's become of her. Come a long way from running the youth club on the council estate. Like him. She is trying to hide in her case from his searching gaze. He gets up, walks level with her.

"This is yours, I think," he says as he turns to run up the stairs. He's late to get his dole money.

She looks at the old tobacco tin. She opens it. Inside is one photo of her and George, and two rings from long ago.

She wanted it all – big office, top job. He just wanted to be with her no matter what. She looks up. There's George on the platform opposite. She closes her case, stands and points to the bridge over the tracks, starts to move as he moves. They meet in the middle of the bridge, her hand reaching out for his, and he lets her lead him away from his lunch-time drink in the park, away from the rest of the dole office drinkers. He won't screw up this time.

IN A ROSEWOOD BOX
L. A. Hollywood

Kirsten sits in the loft, bathed in sunlight that comes through a sky-light. Dust floats around her as she looks through an old trunk – things she's never seen before. She's been left the cottage by her great-aunt, Sheila.

Kirsten's alone in the cottage, a city girl in the Highlands, going through what looks like junk to her. But in one corner of the trunk, on a piece of deep red velvet, is a rosewood box and lots of old letters wrapped in tissue paper. Inside the box are faded yellow silk roses and a pair of pink satin slippers.

Kirsten starts to read the letters. They are all from a man. Out of one of the letters, a photo falls – a picture of her aunt and a man, holding hands, looking straight ahead. He's in a uniform, she in a wedding dress. They stand in front of Duff House.

Her aunt had given her whole life to this man who never returned.

Kirsten reads all the letters, from 1942 to 1945, losing herself in them. And then the last: "Coming home for Christmas, and your birthday, love Aaron." With it, a black-rimmed card which reads, "Captain Aaron McDay, lost at sea, 29/12/45."

Tears run down Kirsten's face, for an aunt and a man she's never met. She re-wraps the things, puts them back in the trunk, and thinks of her husband Don and the lies he's told her when he works away from home.

She goes downstairs to the kitchen, takes off her wedding ring, wraps it in loo paper and puts it in an envelope with a note saying, "I'm staying here." Leaving it by the back door to give to the postman, she feels kind of good inside herself.

KATE
Jackie Liuba

Poor Kate . . . picking fitfully at a strand of hair that was clinging to the back of her neck she lifted the whole heavy mass of it into a band, twisting it in and out and away from any part of her overheated skin. She trembled with tiredness, poking fingers into her hardened neck muscles, tried in vain to lift up her aching pelvic floor and began to clear up the debris of the kitchen. The time left for herself seemed to be less each day, the children demanding stories until they slept. Sometimes she slept before them, sagging, black clothed and overweight into the cushions of the bedside chair.

She scraped thoughtfully at the hardening strand of spaghetti, half-way down the front of her skirt and began stacking the slithering fruit bars back in the cupboard, scooping apple and orange peel into her hand from the worktop, picking dried fruit from the soles of her bare feet . . . the cracks in her heels as painful as razor blade slashes. Putting down the tea towel she looked into the garden over the multi-coloured assortment of children's tea set and mild, blue pots of her own. The orange-berried cotoneaster tackled the overhang of the windowsill to compete with her over-watered geraniums and wilting herb pots and she stared past them into the still light evening.

The roofs of the houses in the Close, once bright burnished copper, were now dull green; they were strangely shaped, like family tents on a campsite, fascinating the eye . . . pulling it different ways, along different planes. Strangely shaped windows protruded at unexpected angles, staring at her darkly, or receded into secret depths to peep and spy. An aeroplane hung in the sky, deceptive as a squirrel's tail. Even taking off, it darkened the sun slowly; sliding through the cloud like a silver bolt slowed by the camera for our delight . . . a dream sequence. The thought calmed her and walking into the next room, she held the clutter at bay by closing the curtains. She placed a table light under the picture, the small glow illuminating its charcoaled depths and, squatting hugely, she tried, yet again, to meditate.

They had bought the picture together and it had become the symbol of desire for her during all those infertile years . . .a mother breastfeeding her child. The head of the child, paper white against the dark shading of the raised jumper, was larger than that of its mother. But the mother's hands were large too, holding her baby safely against her body. During her barren time all her attention would be drawn to the child . . . its bare, vulnerable head, the gently curled fingers that seemed to fondle the breast. She thought that the disproportionate size of the child was representing its supreme importance, the over-emphasised hands, the ability of the mother to meet its every need. But lately, sitting here like a crumpled, black Buddha, she saw only the mother's head . . . unkempt hair, downcast eyes and discontented mouth . . . shrinking, being sucked small by this huge child, this . . . monster.

Monster?

Oh, come now ... whichever one of you has never felt that helpless quiver of fear, when your children don't do as you say . . . has not projected it way into the future, when that blank look of defiance will be aimed at a teacher or the law? Which of you has never looked at them, your own children, climbing, slipperless onto the worktops to rake in the cupboards, ignoring your demands for them to 'come down', never watched them pulling out the fruit bars by the handful and running off, deaf to your demand that they 'put them back', stripping off the papers and dropping them to stick to the already foul floor covering that used to be called a carpet? Which one of you has not felt a whining child pulling at your body as if he owned it, pushing his worryingly thin elbows deep into your breasts, standing between you and the only sane person you've spoken to for days, blocking your view of their mouth, so that you can't even lip read over the din . . . and not wanted to thrust this child, your own child into the corner of the settee . . . to scream into its face that you are sick of it, sick of it . . . your own child? And who of you then has not thought of the woman who threw stair rods at her child, for crumbs on the carpet, and pierced his brain through his eye and spent her life in prison whilst she only wanted to be dead? Which of you has not thought of that when your own child has emptied the Lego box again, and kicked it all around the room because you said he couldn't go outside? And which of you have sat in that room, that child-dominated room with a cave of settee cushions and a wall of child art and looked at your child with hip-hanging jeans, porridge-patterned sweatshirt, draped in pirate/prince remnants and his father's face and not wanted to start again . . . and be stricter this time? Which of you has not felt that moment when your life is obviously all wrong, that your mother had been right?

In the morning she woke to the sound of their voices and knew they would soon come in to her. Opening the curtains slightly she saw her neighbour, beneath the pinkening birch tree, posturing with his silver Tai Chi sword, '. . . slicing day from night', she thought drowsily. And then they were there . . . little bodies 'snuggling', hard little elbows poking and thousands of wet kisses from one . . . the other not so close but needing to be drawn in and held and made to chuckle a bit. Warm human flesh asking for stories 'from your mind' and moving picture books and songs sung with fusty morning breath.

Later, as she put him through the kindergarten gate, he embraced her, arms around the neck . . . twice . . . this boy who already cared so much about his hair, his boots, the way things went together . . . so careful of his dignity. Turning to go she felt his arms around her waist, his face upon her back, and walking away she twisted round to stay locked in those eyes beneath the red hair and baseball cap and was overfilled with love. She bent to pick up the other child, and as she lifted him onto her hip, she noticed her hands. They were not very big . . . but she thought that she would manage, anyway.

COME SUN UP
Jim Piper

It was eleven o'clock, one hour to midnight, when I entered the quiet place. I had a deadline – to write three chapters of my new book by noon the next day. I switched on the light. There, staring up at me, was my old adversary, the Blank Page Kid.

"Blanky, you again. I told you yesterday I've nothing to give. And you just look at me saying nothing. I can't even read between your lines. Why, that stare just gets to me deep inside. Well, Blanky, tomorrow come sun up, meet me here in this quiet place. Just you and me . . ."

I touched my trusty biro in my top pocket.

"You're doomed, Blanky, your time's up."

Blanky just stared back, unbothered. In my mind I felt him say, "Lost for words? Not used to silent retorts?"

I planned my revenge.

"Well, Blanky, at least I'm from a real family. Right now you're just part of the ream, a clone like most of your relatives – apart from the dog-eared or scribbled-on ones. But by sun up, you'll be an individual. A page full of words with such meaning . . . Only then will you truly come to life. Then you will know about communication problems and what it is like to be scrutinised and judged. Your days will be numbered and chaptered."

I lay awake all that night. I could not sleep. What was I going to do about old Blanky – he, who glares at me whenever I go into the room? Silence can be a form of communicative violence. At last, I drifted into a dream.

I saw Blanky just gaping with his nothingness. I thought, "If I wanted to, I could just screw you up into a tiny ball with my bare hands. What would you make of that?"

Blanky glowered saying, "Ah, but I could screw up your mind, your literary life, even your whole career. If I jumped blank out of your printer, you'd crack up."

I wasn't finished with Blanky yet. "I could fold you up and put you in a cheap brown envelope. Post you to the North Pole or the very depths of the Rainforest."

Blanky stayed impressively cool. "You're all words, mate. All fiction, all mistakes, bad grammar and poor punctuation."

Just then, out of the corner of my eye, I spotted Blanky's reinforcements – a whole pad of A4 lined sheets on a chair, poking out from under a cushion. I tried to shout for help but now the words wouldn't even come out of my mouth. I saw an army of lifeless pages forming, waiting to take Blanky's place. At that moment the alarm clock went off.

I woke refreshed and gave myself a mental pep talk. "You've got what it takes, son. In your hands that pen is lethal. You could wipe out Blanky and a hundred more like him."

I raised the mighty biro, my Excalibur. As I did so, the sun rose in the east with an orange light. Well . . . it had inspired Shakespeare. He must have written off reams of Blanky's ancestors.

"Right, Blanky, prepare yourself. Your seconds are numbered. We face each other."

My hand quivered. Blanky gave me his bleakest stare. As I raised my hand over him, I couldn't help but feel some compassion for my old adversary. At a rapid adrenalin-fuelled pace, I delivered the title and first sentence. Then the *coup de grace* – chapters one, two and three – which took care of his swathe of reinforcements. Time for a cup of tea and a chocolate biscuit.

Two weeks later Blanky was cremated on the lounge fire. It's not what he would have wanted, but tough. So to all you blank pages in my care, heed this warning. Your days are numbered.

THE TERM
Sandra Bain

My mother had been crying during the day. As I lay sleepless, wondering what had caused her grief, I became aware of raised voices. That was unusual – except sometimes on a Saturday night when Father had a lapse and drank too much with the other farmhands at the pub. Jeannie's breathing was regular as she lay beside me – sound asleep – and the gentle snoring from the boys' bed assured me that they too were asleep.

I slipped out of bed trying not to make too much noise as I pattered across the bare wooden floor. The door was ajar, enough to enable me to creep out without making the hinges creak. I shivered in the unlit lobby – I wasn't very brave in the dark – but I tiptoed to the door of the other room. My parents were still not in bed and my mother was sobbing. The baby cried out in his sleep. My father lowered his voice and most of the conversation was lost.

Words like 'feeing market', 'better farm', 'bigger cottage' drifted out. Then Mother spoke. She was angry.

"But we've only just moved here. Are you never satisfied? Those children will have yet another change of school . . ."

That was enough and I had to stop myself crying out.

I liked my teacher and didn't want to go to a new school among strangers again. I didn't care about a bigger cottage.

The voices dipped again so I scuttled back to bed. As I crept under the blankets, Jeannie stirred.

"What were you doing?" She was indignant when I passed on the news. "I'm not going! I'll stay here."

"Don't be silly, Jeannie, you're only seven – you can't stay here."

"You can stay with me."

"What are you two talking about?" We had wakened the boys.

"Well, we'll not go either. We can all stay together. We're old enough. We can work on the farm."

We began hatching plans. What would we tell Father and Mother?

Who would ask the farmer to give us work? Would he let us stay in the cottage? Could we run away and hide on the day of the flitting?

Apart from the crackle of the fire and the sound of potatoes for supper boiling on the black range, it was quiet in the little cottage. When the others arrived back bedlam would be let loose. They were with Father helping at the farm. I was always the one who had to stay to help Mother with the baby. I didn't mind.

It had been a tough day at school – keeping our secret. I had wanted to tell my best friend but knew there would be trouble at home if the word spread.

Now I tried to pretend there was nothing wrong but as I rocked the cradle, hoping the baby would go to sleep soon, my mind was churning. Mother must have wondered this morning why her usually boisterous family had been so sullen but perhaps she was glad. She had looked so tired and I reckoned that she hadn't slept much.

"Mam, are we leaving here?"

"Who told you that?" Her voice was sharp.

"Where are we going this time?" She flinched and I thought I had overstepped the mark.

The lowing of the cows signalled the end of milking and their return to pasture. Their hooves drummed as they passed our cottage and they jostled and boxed each other like playful children as they headed for freedom.

"That'll do, lass. Away and fetch the milk from the dairy. And be careful not to spill any." Her eyes filled up with tears as she spoke. I wanted to give her a hug but she turned away and busied herself with the pots on the fire. I picked up the milk pail and trudged down the track to the farm. Although it was May the east wind was sharp. On the way back it bit my face and pierced my thin dress. I had trouble keeping the heavy pail steady, desperately trying not to spill the milk.

Over supper – potatoes and herring, which I detested – Mother was very quiet. She showed little interest in the tales of school and who had got the strap today. She feigned shock on hearing what ignominy the teacher had suffered at the hands of unruly pupils. Father warned us that if he ever heard that we behaved like that we'd know all about it. Jeannie and I helped her clear up and we washed the dishes while the boys fetched water from the well. Father sat back in his chair and lit his pipe but I sensed tension in the air.

The boys were sheepish as they presented pails which were only half full. The rest had spilt as they larked about on the way back.

"You'll have to go for more."

"Aw, Mam! Why can't the girls go? Why do we always have to go to the well? And it's pouring rain."

Father put down his pipe and began to rise. The boys scampered out the door, pails clattering, as they escaped the possible consequences of his wrath.

We were told nothing about the move that night, nor the next night, nor for several nights. It was time to start packing before Mother finally talked to us about what was happening.

"We're not going!"

It was like a shot from a gun. Mother had never before slapped one of the children and the skelp administered to the boy who had dared speak was enough to stop us saying more about our plans.

The sun was rising as the horse and cart were brought to the door. We watched as first the bed ends and then the springs and mattresses were loaded. The dresser needed three men to lift it and so did the kitchen table. Chairs were stacked, the cradle followed and then the trunk with our clothes. There were a few small boxes containing other possessions.

"But where are we going to sit?" Jeannie was whining. Mother gave a funny smile.

Father said that we were not going far; but we had heard that last time and it had taken us nearly a day's travelling.

Just as he spoke, an open-topped car appeared along the lane and stopped at our house. A car? The driver jumped out and opened all the doors.

"Right, yous lot. In you all get." We hesitated but mother, with the baby in her arms, went into the front and Father pushed the rest of us into the back. The doors were shut; the driver manoeuvred the car and we were off, waving to Father and the men with the cart. What excitement! We gently rubbed the leather seats and touched the wood trimming on the doors. We couldn't believe that we were in a car. We gazed around as the countryside sped past and we felt important. Hair streamed in the wind and I noticed the boys' eyes were shining.

At the feeing market some farmers offered better wages but in Father's case a bigger cottage had been the deal. But Father also knew that his new employer had a reputation for being kind to his men. Sending a car for the family was evidence.

In what seemed a very short time we were driving up to a farmhouse overlooking the sea. We were met by a friendly lady who turned out to be the farmer's wife. She took us into a large room where there was the biggest table I had ever seen. Mother told us this was the dining-room and cautioned us to be on our best behaviour. We were too overawed to be anything else.

A maid came in with plates of corned-beef sandwiches, glasses of milk for the children and a pot of tea for Mother. We were hungry, as usual, and the sandwiches were delicious.

When the food was all gone, the farmer's wife suggested to Mother that she let us go down to explore the seashore and they could call us when the furniture arrived. Mother warned us not to get wet because all our other clothes were on the cart.

We played there a long time before we heard Father calling us. The cart had arrived.

We raced back to the house.

"Oh, Mam, it's wonderful down at the sea!"

"There is sand and ..."

"... and fish and ..." We all wanted to talk at once.

"Can we go every day?"

"I'm sure you can. But now it's time to see your new home."

Everything had been unloaded and put into the cottage. It was a much bigger place than our last one.

Excitement mounted when we discovered there was a scullery, separate from the kitchen, and it had a sink with taps.

"No more trips to the well!" The boys ran around chanting, "No more trips to the well."

"And no more carrying pails of milk!" I stared at my father. "Mam is going to help in the dairy and she'll take home the milk."

"Mam is going to work at the farm, too?"

"That's right. We're going to be well off."

My mother, her eyes sparkling, took my arm and drew me through the lobby to a door I hadn't noticed before.

"How would you like this little room for yourself?" My own bedroom!

And finally I realised that my father and mother would never have moved without good reason. How could we have been so daft as to think they would?

HERON
Christina Macdonald

I see him from the shore,
The old grey man, back again,
Pacing up and down,
Hands clasped behind,
What is he waiting for
Out there in the grey mud?

Is he doing what we humans do –
Waiting for the country bus that never seems to come?
I watch him.
Grey feathers neatly tucked behind tall spare body,
The church elder
Upright, contained.
A certain sharpness of intellect
Suggested by his piercing beak.
He takes no cognizance of me,
Or if he does, chooses to ignore my curiosity.
Alone, he dominates the landscape by the shore,
Stepping elegantly through grey, clinging mud.
Like a man with brand-new shoes.
He stares across the grey expanse of tidal firth
Towards the distant bridge
Waiting for in-coming tide
To bring him little fishes for his tea
Or just contemplating the meaning of it all?
Continuing my walk along the path
He is still there when I return
But now his profile's changed –
Hunched up, horizontal, he's lost his poise.
He stands still, dejectedly resigned.
Do herons get depressed I wonder?

WAVE
Henriette A.O. Stewart

R oll. Roll. Forwards, backwards. Touching the beach, the cliffs, the harbour wall. Moving along the edge of dry land. Always in motion, approaching, retreating. Restless, restless.

"I have only ever seen the edge of the continent. I long to see what is in there, behind the dunes." The restless wave crashed aimlessly onto the beach, making foam.

The other waves looked at him worriedly.

"Oh no, you know very well that us waves are not meant to venture inland," they told him. "You must be content with what you can see from here."

Content the restless wave was not, even at high tide. It rushed back into the ocean, moving against the current where the other waves told it to be sensible.

"You should be thankful that you are not just fresh water in some stagnant pond," they said. "Be proud you were made to lap."

The restless wave headed for the deepest, darkest part of the ocean. The place it had always been told never to go, and therefore the most appealing place to go when in a rebellious mood. Cold, dark, lonely.

"No one understands me, they are not even trying. Why won't they listen to me?"

"We are listening," said voices deep below the ocean floor.

"Who are you?" asked the wave.

"We are the fault lines. You may not have heard about us. Everyone tries to forget about us."

"Why?"

"Because we are bad." The fault lines started to laugh, gratingly, crushingly, until bubbles of hot air began pouring up from the crust. The laughter subsided and the bubbles died away. "We can help you," they said.

"How?"

"We have ways. Trust us. Go back to your beach and wait; it will happen very soon."

The restless wave rose up, buoyed by bubbles from the fault lines' laughter, and returned to the beach where it joined the other waves. The tide was receding and the waves were falling back. Feathered creatures landed on the wet sand and began looking for food; two-legged creatures pushed out small boats or settled on the beach, playing in the sand.

Then a silent shiver went through the ocean and the waves barely had time to wonder what had happened, when they were pulled further away from the beach. The restless wave was dragged back, exposing beach never before exposed, desperately trying not to, bewildered at this reversal.

The pulling stopped. For a moment the ocean swirled in a weightless, timeless manner. Then the surge. Rushing, roaring. What elation, what triumph! As one, the waves soared to a great height and moved up the beach over the dunes, inland, going forwards, onwards. The restless wave made sure to push itself right to the front and gleefully crashed onto roads and into buildings, ecstatic at the sensory bombardment of new smells and tastes. It ripped up trees and discarded them just as quickly, leaving them to churn in the waves behind. Oh, this was too much, too good to be true! Bliss! Excitement! Feel like doing this every day, all the time. Yes, now, forever!

Before the restless wave had time to appreciate this alien upland world properly, the ocean stopped pushing, and slowly, gently, withdrew.

"What a short pleasure that was," the restless wave complained to no one in particular.

The wave beside rocked and exclaimed, "Do you call this pleasure? Look around you."

The restless wave looked.

"I can't see anything for all this debris. And look at the colour of us, if you're not blue then I guess I am not either."

No one laughed. The restless wave swirled past a house and glanced in the window.

"What's wrong with all the land creatures? Why are they just floating about like that? We're going to end up carrying them out with us."

But no one answered. No one talked, just glided silently, slithered apologetically back towards the beach, unwillingly carrying with them the fruits of their destruction.

THE FALSE NOSE
Vivien Samet

The student of psychology cycled past Edinburgh's Museum of Modern Art on a wintry Sunday morning just a few days after the New Year. The scene reminded him of a leftover Christmas card. He was pedalling at such a speed that a poster advertising the current Magritte exhibition was too blurred to decipher. However, he subconsciously registered an image of a bowler-hatted man with a face showing a green apple in place of his nose.

Impulsively he pressed the brakes of his bicycle which screeched to a halt as if crying out for a dose of 'Three in One' oil. He was subsequently thrown over the handlebars, landing in the snow alongside his knitted scarf of mauve, yellow and crimson stripes.

Dazed, he picked up his bike and also the soggy muffler, adjusted his glasses and leaned against the black iron railings to study the poster. The words, 'René Magritte – A Key to Dreams', leapt out at him, settling in his imagination along with the artist's famously surreal images.

Noticing that the gallery was open from 3pm until 6pm he figured he could cycle back to his flat, collect money for his entrance fee and after a bite to eat return in time to see this exhibition by one of the great twentieth century contemporary painters. As he stood at the entrance gates, easing his cycling gloves over his frozen hands, he looked up just in case he might catch a glimpse of those Magritte baguettes floating high in the sky like clouds.

He realised he should have been spending the morning on his psychology thesis as the final part of his doctorate was looming near. On his cycle ride home a thought occurred to him relating to some practical research he might carry out while viewing the exhibition, thus combining work and pleasure.

The experiment would entail viewing Magritte's fantastical pictures while wearing a false nose. This would test viewers' reactions as the psychology student strolled through the gallery. These he would jot down in his red leather notebook kept solely for the purpose of

'Human Behaviour Observations' – providing a source of analysis and reference for his thesis.

Returning to his flat he ferreted out a selection of false noses. The Magritte look was finally completed after discovering a black bowler hat and pair of wire-framed spectacles in his research box. Studying his reflection in the gilt-framed hall mirror he had an uncanny feeling he was viewing an original painting. Only the blinking of his eyelids spooked him into grabbing his black overcoat, fixing a pair of cycle-clips around his ankles and cycling back to the exhibition, false nose in place and wearing his black bowler hat.

By now it was snowing hard, but the student was undeterred and battled through blizzard conditions, wheels skidding on the slippery cobbled stones of historic Edinburgh, his colourful scarf standing out against the white background. At the traffic lights drivers who were previously so absorbed in the navigation of their vehicles in near white-out conditions failed to notice the student's strange appearance.

He was nearing the entrance to the Museum of Modern Art when a speeding car with lights flashing overtook the other vehicles before pulling in alongside him. The student was overcome with excitement. At last, he thought, a reaction!

The police officer leaned out of his car window and yelled, "Excuse me sir, but are you not aware that your bicycle has a puncture?"

THE COLLECTION
June Munro

When people refer to 'the collection' when speaking of our church service I seldom think of the offertory. What the word collection conjures up for me is the congregation. Sparse though it is, the congregation is a collection of characters par excellence and I greatly admire our Minister who never indicates by a word or a look what a motley crew we are. Visiting ministers are not always so discreet. Some have been known to blanche at the sight of one particular worshipper, striding down the aisle towards 'her' seat at the front. One minister is remembered for the tears she shed when she arrived – unexpectedly turning out to be female and therefore not acceptable to one lady parishioner. Lindsey, usually being accepted in these parts to be a male name, had caused some confusion and the unfortunate 'lady minister' was made to feel so unwelcome that she never came back.

My favourite is the tall, elderly, Canadian minister who came looking for his roots many years ago and stayed on. A warm sensible man he lost marks with the church treasurer when he was found taking a dram in the vestry after the service. In the winter temperatures in our kirk who would blame him?

But enough of the ministers . . . the stars sit in the pews. Bright-eyed and bushy-tailed, miserable, hung-over or just plain thrawn – all human life is there.

We have the Blairs, Judy and Jim, both looking earnest, slightly beatnik and not very tidy. Devoted to saving the planet and aiding all of Africa by themselves. Too busy travelling abroad to help their elderly parents, but then the neighbours do that. You know, the ones that don't go to church.

Behind them is Margery Brown – 'Lady Margery' to the cynical – pillar of the church, the WRI, the Autumn Leaves Club and self-appointed spokesperson for the village. Margery does a lot of good, but never by stealth.

Behind her sit the Andersons; he's years older than she is, retired Bank Manager. Nobody knows what she does, but she is always dressed to the nines and there are rumours . . .

Last on that side is Morag Cameron, last surviving member of the Camerons of Invercockaleekie, round as a ball, hair dyed an impossible shade of red, all kaftans and scarves and smelling of incense and mothballs. People refer to her as 'Poor Morag' but are disabused of any need for sympathy should they cross her, or forget who she is – or was.

On 'our' side sit the more sensible members of the congregation. Big Davy MacDougall from Cnoc Dhu – buttons on his tweed jacket strained almost to bursting over his belly. Davy only wears a tie on Sundays and that goes into his pocket when he gets back into his Land Rover after the service. He can't sing, needs glasses to read the words of the hymns but he broke his pair last Christmas and can't be bothered replacing them. On top of that he doesn't believe in God any more and only comes to get away from his wife Betty. 'The Moaner of the Glen' he calls her.

Sadie and Sandy Fraser sit hand in hand in front of Davy. "Married for 50 years and never a cross word," is their boast, but Sandy being deaf as a post must help and Sadie has never believed the gossip about Sandy and Wilma Black that has gone about the place for years.

Mrs Wilson sits right at the front, almost nose to nose with the Minister, who eschews the pulpit in favour of the lectern standing just in front of the first pew. I always think he is particularly brave to stand there where his every move, breath or word is under such close scrutiny. Mrs Wilson takes no prisoners . . . the slightest deviation from the text of the Good Book is noted and referred to as she shakes hands after the service. An unfamiliar hymn tune is complained about, and suitability of the sermon commented upon. Mrs Wilson sees herself as the true guardian of Christianity in Corrie.

The last pew is usually occupied by myself – the incomer. I married into Corrie some thirty years ago and people still wonder why my Donald had to go to the West Coast to find a bride. I don't really belong; I am accepted by few, tolerated by most, but given another thirty years, I may, just may become a local, a part of the collection.

JEAN ARMOUR'S LAMENT
Valerie Weir

My bonny Rab ye've had your day.
Noo it's weemen that haud sway,
it's time folks heard o your puir wife
wha had sax bairns an sic a life
as wadna been tholed by ony wumman
wha'd had the mense tae see it comin.
Nae pint in gaun for 'kiss an tell'.
Yours is a life that's kent ower well
or mibby no; *it gars me greet*
the warld aye thocht my life was sweet
for I'd the man that they aa wantit
–'The Bard' – wha'd had 'Kilmarnock' prentit.
– But that same lad wham nane surpasses
for hochmagandy wi the lasses
wis gey sweir tae settle doun
an ettled sail for Kingston toun
– for sun an sea an – rum, I'll wage thee
forby the thocht ye micht win free
o Mary an me (ye'd bairned us baith)
– whame'er ye'd chuse there'd be some skaith!
Then twins I bure, a lad an lass
an twa lang years were lettit pass
afore we mairrit, an aa that while
ye'd been taen up wi yon hure's smile
scrievin sangs an a wheen verses.
For onie sake! Her name was Agnes
an no Clarinda! Sic a fancy
cam frae taiglin wi the gentry.
Syne, deil kens why, ye tak a ferm
for weary darg an nocht but herm.
At Ellisland we'd twins aince mair
athin fower weeks were in a lair.
They dwined an widna thrive thir twa,
near braks my hert noo they're awa.

Ellisland sae unforgein
wi ill-faured parks an plowterin.
Nae maitter how ye'd ferm or scrieve
ye'd mak less siller nor a grieve
sae in the year o eichty-nine
ye taks a job as exciseman
but your daft talk o Revolution
aamaist costs ye your promotion
an William here for me tae nurse
alang wi Anna's puir wee lass
– anither o your bastart bairns.
For this o Rab thou'll get thy fairins!
But Guid be thanked for 'Tam o Shanter'
by-ornar guid, a worthy ranter
wha wan us siller for the flittin
intae the toun an oor new sittin.
The Excise here ye owersee
an organise the Volunteers.
A birkie on a steerie horse
oot in weather snell an coorse
aye drookit, ye're sin taen ill.
The doctor's ca'd tae mak ye hale
but ye'll no mend whate'er we dae
an we've tae watch ye dwine away.
Wee Maxwell's born that time o day
your kist is laid doun in the clay.
Yon gentle verses, some for me
will ne'er again be scrieved by thee.
Your fiddle's quaited on the wa.
Nae cantie sangs soun thro' the ha
juist greetin sair frae aa that mourn
oor Rabbie that will ne'er return.
Noo wha this tale o woe shall read,
bonny lasses aa tak heed.
Whene'er tae luve your thochts are turnin
mind, Jeannie scrieved this for a warnin!

THE LEAVING
Carol Fenelon

Here there was a silence you could lean against. It was almost tangible, touchable even, wrapped up with the dark, dank smell of the nearly empty room. Karen cast her eyes across to the box lying beneath the window. It lay seemingly forgotten, half-covered by a scarf she had left behind in her flight from the island. She had been given the scarf by another lover and she smiled at the incongruity of it all. The draught from the window whispered against the filthy net curtain as it scratched at the stained wooden box top in a desultory fashion.

It seemed a very strange place to be. Although she had lived only a very small part of her life there she had left an unexpectedly, achingly large piece of herself wrapped in this house. She had not expected the call telling her he was dead. She had thought that, after five years in the clear, he would have lived forever nearly. The thought of this kind of leaving, this brutal finality, had never become part of her conscious mind. She still felt shaken by the thought that he no longer walked the long road to the lighthouse, no longer pottered about the house half-dressed for hours in the early morning before she had even surfaced. These habits had become hooks on which to hang the aching in her heart and meant early mornings could still be shared, albeit in a very separate fashion.

The room felt deserted. No collection of stones to clutter up the side of the sink. No pheasant feather sticking out of an old bottle on the windowsill. The carpet caught at her toe the way it always had and the action of rebalancing felt like something she had done a million times. Looking out in the garden she felt him to be there mirroring her glance, also puzzled at what had happened to them, the aloneness they had both ultimately chosen.

She had not come to the funeral. She knew she would not have been welcome, was still seen as the rat who had deserted the sinking ship. She had never been able to tell more than one or two people why she had gone back to the mainland. More than that would have been the very worst kind of betrayal of the very private kind of person Callum was. She had made the journey now in order to pick up the small pieces of her life she had left behind and to sever the cord that had attached them, one to another, for what had seemed like her whole life.

The lighthouse stared blankly back at her when she looked out the window, holding the curtain back with an uncertain finger. The box lay quietly at her feet, a covering of grime showing there had been no betrayal, that her hand would be both the first and the last to touch it. She knelt down carefully on the green, faded carpet and breathed a long sigh. There was so much of her past locked both inside herself and this wooden kist. Such a box would have held the hopes and dreams of the travellers to the new world, new linen for a new bride. She smiled wryly. He had not wanted to marry her yet, when he was lost in his alcohol-fuelled dreams, he would call her his wife. To this she had said nothing. A sober proposal was never made other than he would marry her if she really wanted him to. It had felt like a challenge rather than a loving desire and anyway the bindings that held them had been both a curse and a blessing without a piece of paper. So much had been said and yet not said, done and yet not done.

This kist was all he had left her. The rest of his possessions, her possessions also, were gone leaving the house almost bare. To his children had gone the sentimental trivia that would hold their father a little closer from time to time, evidence of his itinerant life around a sometimes unkind world. The rest of the assorted debris with which he had surrounded himself during the last years of his quiet, solitary existence had gone to the skip. She smiled at the thought of the hands that would trawl through it avariciously. Even the least particle would be handled and its usefulness discussed with a great earnestness.

Her careful finger enquired at the lock and it gave with a sudden willingness, as if it were glad to reveal its secrets. The gaping lid revealed the brass lamp she had left behind and the oval mirror she had somehow not had the courage to ask for back. Two sketches of Skye lay carefully wrapped in what was left of an old flannelette sheet and underneath that were the items she was looking for. There, in two shoeboxes in serried rows, lay the letters she had written to him, the cards she had sent. Words of love, need, and a one-time all-consuming lust, all upended and open to the elements as the beaks of newly hatched chicks. She felt her own vulnerability as she ran her fingers over the envelopes, noting they had all been opened with the very sharp penknife he had always carried in his back pocket. In touching them she felt she was touching him, and she shut her eyes for a long moment. The smell that had been his seemed to permeate the room and her head bowed in a silent acknowledgment of this presence. She felt the letters to be virginal, that the prying eyes who might have wanted to sully her memory, who might have passed the words from person to person and even laugh at what they revealed, had not been given access. That, in the end, he had loved her enough to protect her from this final indignity and for that she was grateful. She would read them later. It was enough for now to drag the box across the room and out into the low afternoon sun. She shivered slightly as she emerged from the gloom of the house, even though it was warmer outside. She hauled the kist into the boot of the car with a very determined grunt and as she clicked the boot safely shut she smiled. She had not been certain he would keep her safe. She had thought he would have tried.

Turning slowly her eye caught the shape of the ferry in the distance. The view she had now was the view she had had every day as she had waited here, for change or escape, not knowing which she had really wanted. She had loved him truly beyond reason, had held him in her heart during all the years they could not be together and now she had to let him go. She slipped into the driving seat, turned the car slowly and drove carefully along the pot-holed road that led from the lighthouse to the cemetery. As she passed she saw the flowerings that covered him and she held the view in her eyes for a moment as it slid past her. Then she joined the new road along to Port Ellen, to the pier and her route home. She saw no one she knew as she drove through the small village that had been her home for a very brief time and parked in the line of cars at the ferry terminal. She already had her ticket; she had bought a return from the mainland. Getting out of the car she stood quietly at the edge of the pier, watching the ferry make its final approach, feeling as though she were made of fine spun glass, as though everyone around could see her innermost thoughts, feel her innermost feelings.

Aware of the smell, that fishy seaweedy smell of boats and nets and the paraphernalia of a working pier, she turned her head and as she did so the lighthouse caught her eye. It lay square and squat across the bay. She felt as though she could reach out and touch it, that it was breathing almost imperceptibly, waiting for her to leave and that when the ferry carried her away it would straighten up with a sigh of relief.

To its right she could see the Grey House. It had a real name but for her it would always be the Grey House. The windows winked back at her in the morning sunshine, shining blindly, shutting out the outside world and no one could see in. She didn't need to see in. She could see it all and smell it all even with her eyes shut. She knew that it would be imprinted on her mind, held in her heart for a long time, forever perhaps.

She pulled open the door of her car and slipped in, shutting it quietly. The click of the door felt very loud. She did not want to draw attention to herself. As the queue of cars shuffled forwards she shrank farther into her jacket. She was waiting for someone, anyone, to tap her on the shoulder and berate her for deserting a sinking ship, that Callum had needed her and what was her problem with that? That the way he had lived and drank was the way many folk lived on the island and that in leaving she had not only judged and condemned Callum, she had judged and condemned them all. How she had longed, sometimes, to be able to join in the slow, soporific, laziness of it all. She too had longed to shut out the reality of what their lives had become.

Karen took her time in pulling her pack of tobacco out of her bag. The familiar rhythm of rolling a cigarette between her fingers, one that had become very unfamiliar over the last few months with Callum, comforted her and as she lit the cigarette she felt a sense of calm wash over her. The line of cars crept forward and soon she was in the belly of the ship. It was at this moment she felt herself to be at her most vulnerable. She would have to get out of the car and walk upstairs to the saloon to sit with the other passengers, mostly islanders.

Shunning the bar she chose to stand outside at the rail and watch as the ship nosed its way across the bay past the Grey House, past the lighthouse holding its breath, turning to port and heading for the mainland. How many times had Karen watched the ferry do this while sitting in the house, looking out of those same windows? She had longed to be on the ferry, to escape from Callum and when she had finally left him her sense of despair had been as immense as her sense of relief.

She knew why she was standing at the rail. Other times she had gone to the mainland Callum would stand in the garden and wave to the ferry as it went by. While he could just make out the small dot that was her, she saw him quite clearly. It had been good to see him waiting and waving on the return journey as well but latterly he had not bothered, not really wanting her to return. He had wrapped himself in his own small world as he fought his own sickness within, the cancer eating at his throat, and she had become an awkward extra in the detail of his life.

She did not cry then as she passed the place she had tried to make home. She almost saw him in the garden waving but she knew it could only be her imagination, her longings for what should have been, not what really had been. She hardened herself for the leaving. She drew on a cigarette and blew it defiantly towards the house, towards the garden she had made, towards the blinking window where she had always hoped he might have been watching and despairing for her return.

When she went into the cafeteria her eyes flicked nervously across the room looking for anyone who might see her, know her, attack her possibly. Recognising only Mhairi, the barmaid from the inn where Callum used to drink, she breathed out and joined the slow-moving queue waiting to buy a greasy breakfast, a tepid tea, a tasteless coffee. The breakfast never changed, nor did the dinner menu of macaroni cheese, chicken curry or steak pie.

She remembered Callum had been angry with her for leaning over to steal a chip while she waited for a bacon roll, had been angry when she had sat talking to a man who, like herself, walked with a stick. He had been angry about a lot of things. The coffee tasted just as bad as ever and she went out on to the top deck to pass the journey.

The ship felt claustrophobic and the guilt she had felt at leaving him when he had needed her, the sense of panic that she had been living with came with her, and sat with her, and wrapped itself around her until she felt slow tears slip down her face, dripping down to create a slowly spreading dark blood-like stain on the warm red of her jacket.

DAFFODILS BY THE WALL
L. A. Hollywood

Ann sits in her old rocking chair by the back door of her cottage in the late sun, which throws a shadow across the garden. She looks at the daffodils by the wall. The yellows and reds make her think back to the Dutch fishermen who came over so long ago when the herring were running. They were both so young then, her Alec back at sea just nine days. She dreams of those times more and more these days. She still loves the two men that have both gone from her.

She sits there in the sun. They are not the same flowers he brought over with him. No, these ones came from a shop. But they take her back – to that summer sixty years ago and the nine days and eight nights with Robert.

He had a wife back home, like she had a husband at sea.

Ann looks at the sun setting, then moves to put the kettle on for tea. She is waiting for her grandsons to come for the last time this year. Standing in the doorway, she looks down the garden to the washing line, with its hooks ready for the herring, and the bucket of salty water. Ann hears them coming round the side of the cottage, six baskets hanging from their oars. As they go by waving, she looks at Robert with his light brown hair, blue eyes and easy grin, then Alec with his green eyes and dark hair. Both have something from the grandfathers they never knew. She watches them hanging the herring to dry before it is boxed up for the mainland. Next year they'll be taking them across the island to the new smoke house. Then she'll sell the cottage, move into town and split the money three ways between them.

A POETRY EXPERIENCE
Jackie Liuba

Minty was trying to get out of the bag again – she felt him as she reached in to get a mint. That's how he'd got his name – pulled out, by accident, after lying for months next to a packet of Polos.

"You smell minty," she'd said. Smaller than her hand, a puce, crimplene, horse-like thing with a maroon, woollen mane and tail, he'd rolled his eyes at her and smirked.

They'd had adventures together. She had written about them as through the eyes of a child – 'Minty and Me'. He was a *character*. Well, when they can't be bothered to put a price on you, even in a charity shop – you have to do *something* to get noticed! "Not always a very *nice* character," she thought, ignoring his writhing in the depths of her bag.

Even this holiday had been his idea.

"Come on," he'd said, rustling around in her Sunday paper. "Let's go to the Canaries and write silly poems about people mooning about, chewing their pencils and stressing themselves up to write poetry that no-one can understand but themselves."

Tenerife was preparing for carnival the day they all arrived. They were to spend the night there to 'soak up atmosphere' before 'seeking the solace' of the hills and were soon to be seen – small groups of pale women, wandering the streets, waiting for something to begin. "Am I like that?" she thought. "Am I waiting for something to begin?"

Surprised by the early darkness, she found herself suddenly engulfed by small girls draped in sequins and feathers, holding themselves stiff with importance, as their mothers carried them, like tiny princesses, to place them on floats that had grown peach-coloured roses and attracted hundreds of multi-coloured birds. Smells of burnt sugar and singed meat enticed her down the street into a huddle of old ladies stuffed into long curling wigs and satin crinolines, holding furry red masks on sticks, like pince-nez, up to humourless eyes that stared

59

at her as she passed. Swarthy young women with high breasts and bulging calves came close and pouted threateningly into her face – until she saw that they were men and felt afraid.

A spectral cloud of exhaust fumes rose over the dancing area, its excited swirling picked out by the hanging lanterns that also illuminated the plump dancers. Locked together they polkaed tightly round the floor like clockwork dolls wound up for the evening, their fixed expressions of almost boredom indicating that dancing here was a serious business not to be attempted by tourists.

Next morning, as they trod on each others heels, getting onto the bus, she watched the huge palm leaves, that she'd always seen in pictures cooling royal brows, being used to sweep the square; the men, holding them one handed as they smoked, stared, unsmiling, at their departure to their mountain retreat. As she fumbled in her bag she came across him; peering in, she saw that he had a guilty look on his face. He wriggled slightly as she touched him.

"I blame you for this, Minty," she said.

It had started out as he had predicted; she soon realised that she was the only one who had come alone. She was encouraged to join them, of course, over the morning rolls and apricot jam, but her conversational contributions seemed to have an edge that startled them slightly and they began to avoid her. They whispered and linked arms; she heard them laughing together in their shared rooms.

Thrown back on Minty for company, she found it impossible to be serious about this whole sorry attempt to 'find herself' as a writer. She tried to be 'quiet within herself', to allow herself to be 'carried like a leaf on the bed of a stream' but he was always there – haunting her, stalking her, stirring up the ridiculous with his 'cute' little puce hoof. All her 'craters' were filled with 'taters', her 'rock pools' gazed into by 'old fools'.

Ruth, herself, was 'a gift' – narrow-nosed and slightly goitred, her protruding eyes blinking furiously with earnest soul-searching as she cajoled them, from beneath her dark-dyed fringe, to reveal intimacies and hurts, past and present. Metaphor, simile – barren landscapes reminding them of wasted lives; craters waiting to erupt, of their suppressed jealousies; the black sand becoming their eternal disappointment.

Minty was delighted, of course.

"They are *so* sad," he said, drooping down into his Eeyore pose then peering up from between exhausted ears. "Let's *us* have an Adventure." He sidestepped around the desk in the spotlight of the angle-poise lamp. "You could fall into the volcano crater and I could save you by grabbing your knicker elastic – it could be a kind of bungee jumping experience . . ."

She stuffed him into the pocket of her dressing gown and tried to produce something to read out the following day, but all her islands were 'romantic,' her skies were 'sunset-laden' and, of course, her volcanoes – slept.

Days passed. They walked self-consciously behind Ruth through the terraced fields, feeling the hostility of leather-skinned peasants and begging children. They took a bus up the steep mountain tracks – the driver avoiding yellow painted extremities of rocks, which protruded into the road – and walked back down through mist-filled woods of dripping leaves. They sat eating figs beside water that threw itself against smooth-faced rocks and sprayed them with icy droplets. Minty wanted to fall in, to be carried off by a bird, to be left behind, to be found by a child who would take him home. The others scribbled in their notebooks, bit their nails or sat with inward-looking eyes, and she flailed about in her inability to just 'be'.

"Damn you, Minty," she muttered and pushed him down to the bottom of her rucksack.

A trip to the volcano started among eucalyptus trees, where they trampled the sweet smell from the strangely foreign leaves, led on through pathways of ever sparser vegetation until she could see, through spikes of dried brushwood and cartoon cacti, the bare, black summit. She let the others go ahead; watched them file dutifully up the well-trodden path; join others approaching from another point – stayed there kicking ash and seeing little point in carrying on. A thin dog came and sniffed her, bared its teeth and slunk away.

In the evenings, aided by shadow and increasing companion-ability, they would share their over-elaborate, sometimes pompous, often clichéd poetic struggles and she judged them, coldly and silently. She began to re-examine the plausibility of some of Minty's proposed escapades. She reached into her bag to give him a reassuring tickle and – froze. From the darkness behind a wavering candle flame, accompanied by the rasping noises of a foreign night, a soft, hesitant voice began.

"Come into the garden . . . " The words, perfectly chosen, perfectly joined, slipped into her mind like molten joy – no volcanoes or flamingo-headed flowers, no heat, no pride, no epic tale – no rhyme. Just strawberries – a garden, a little piece of life and – love.

She found that she was trembling, her cheeks, somehow, were wet. Minty squirmed uncomfortably between her fingers but, for once, had nothing at all to say.

AUTUMN CAMEO
Christina Macdonald

I am sitting in the summer-house overlooking the large rambling garden, reading the play which the local Amateur Dramatic Group is to present in the village hall next year. I flip over the pages without enthusiasm.

I find myself quite unable to get into the phrase 'It is Sunday morning, Spring' when here I am looking out on my beloved garden just beginning to lift its cool green skirts revealing the yellow, red and orange petticoats of autumn.

Spring may be full of promise but autumn is the realisation, the reality, the proof of the promise teasingly offered. Here, the natural year is at its high point, its zenith. The air today is warm and still. Storms may be raging across the Atlantic, bearing down on tiny islands, lashing trees, smashing homes – here we are completely still.

I love the autumn, perhaps because I was born in October. Some think of autumn as the dying of the year. I think of the year coming to ripeness, fruition. I understand and share Keats' description, 'season of mists and mellow fruitfulness.'

The earth is warm. Orange humble bees and light-winged hover-flies suck and flit among the fading flowers. Michaelmas daisies in purple, bloom. Pink ice-plants sprawl ungainly on the ground and delphiniums bear a second flowering of small mauve spikes.

Against the fence the pyracantha, in summer a white lacy froth of blossom, now seduces little birds with small red fruits. Beyond the wall, a rowan droops low, dripping its heavy burden of fruit to tempt the thrush. I smell wood smoke and, turning, see curls and wisps rising from a nearby golden field.

Soon there will be leaves to rustle in the woods by the ancient beech. Soon the curtains will be early drawn and fires and lamps lit before tea. The year is changing fast, curling up, preparing for slumber in the darkened, sun-deserted days. But now I sit here savouring it all. How very far away the scene 'It is Sunday morning, Spring.'

EATING THE GODS
Heather MacLeod

It is early, an intense winter's day, still as a caught bird. The promise of sun and the first fall of snow has brought the hills closer, making everything more real, adding new dimension.

Rachel collects the eggs before breakfast. Brown and smooth, one is still warm, unusually large with a pointed speckled end. Tapping the big egg three times against the bowl, she prises her thumbs into the sharp gashed edge and pulls, anticipating the slow translucent slide and a yolk the colour of whin blossom. The shell splits neatly and not one but two yolks slip into the bowl, floundering in a sea of watery white. She stares at them in surprise. Not only because there are two, but each holds a tiny pale circle, like a small moon orbiting a great planet. And from each moon, a reticulum of blood vessels pulses out over the smooth yellow surface. She studies them carefully, as if divining their meaning, before they trace her back . . . to Oxford, and Aberdeen. Feeling nausea rising, she leans over the sink, spits then retches.

When she recovers, Rachel cracks two more eggs, cold and fresh, into the glass bowl, and whisks them round until finally the yolks break, the blood mixes in and the little moon foetuses are hidden. Calling Joe and Ella to the table, they eat the eggs, scrambled, with toast.

After breakfast, they prepare for a walk, just the two of them. Rachel needs it to clear her mind. Her dream of the night before and the business with the egg unsettles her. Joe stays behind. It's nice to have him around for a while. While she helps Ella into boots and jacket, she steals glances at him through the half-open door. Already, he's sharpening her favourite knife. She watches as he picks up the stone and spits on the dull surface, before laying the bare blade against it. Then, like a musician drawing a bow across taut strings, he whets it, backwards and forwards, his spittle fanning out, the steel singing out its crescendoing scales to the stone.

Coming out to piss against the garden wall, he says to Ella, "Chicken tonight!" and winks. It's her favourite. Ella tries to wink back, crinkling up her lovely blue eyes in air so cold and dense that Rachel can taste it. Joe's words feel like his hot urine stinging the snow. She knows which bird is for the kill.

They set out before the sun has risen above the mountain. Ella's blue boots squeak as the cold envelops them, seeping between the folds of jackets, burning cheeks and fingers. They smile and stumble, unaccustomed to the track's unyielding nature. Yesterday's wet moss and malleable prints have solidified overnight, jarring every step. Puddles are frozen and dead twigs ejaculate frigid feathery spurts, geometrically perfect. Ella slides and stamps. The ice shatters.

Along the burn, the lower branches of the alder scrub are tide-marked with debris. Dead grass and bits of silage bags hang stiff and glittering, like corn dollies and prayer rags, offerings to the gods. Rachel has a sudden longing to hang something there herself and frantically searches her pocket. But . . . no. And as a slight wind rattles the debris, it rasps where she'd expected bells.

Prancing like an early fawn, Ella runs on, suddenly sun-drenched as orange rays break over the horizon. Rachel follows slowly, running a gloved hand over the tall brittle grasses which frame the track. With the rising warmth, the frozen gerbes ping apart in violent sparkle, dancing and dazzling like a hundred roman candles, surprising her, catching her off-guard. She hears the plip and sigh of the ground beneath. This crisp white surface is a deception.

She is remembering another. A white ceiling, honeycombed and false, behind which she had seen the mass of pipes and tubes that snaked from theatre to ward, keeping pace with the pulse of life. She'd lain alone, before they wheeled her in, staring up and tracing paths through its dark labyrinth. Until an anaesthetist had appeared and she'd surprised herself by bursting into tears. And afterwards, when she had woken, she was still crying. For what? She'd felt no attachment to the cells dividing within her nor to the liaison which made them. When offered, she'd refused counselling. It was her own fault, for god's sake. A stupid mistake.

"Look! An angel!" Ella cries, startling her back to the present. She follows the outstretched arm to a hanging fallen branch. There's no mistaking the demure misericord child-figure in the split timber, hands clasped over pleated gown, noble wings neatly folded, surveying the frost-shrouded bracken below. There's another figure, too, that only she sees. This one contorted, great lime-green fissures veining its limbs. It is naked, head flung back, its desperate struggling arms reaching heavenward.

They turn for home. Ella's constant irrepressible babble hangs in great breaths. Truth or dare. Truth or dare. She dares Rachel to eat snow from the bank, Rachel dares her to sit bare-bummed on the track. She squeals, her rosy cheeks dimpling, her laughter cracking the icy air. "Now truths," Ella says. But from the scrub comes a sika's whistle, and in the break of branches, Rachel catches the quick flick of escape.

Joe had never wanted children, she knew that. It would interfere too much with his work as a travel writer. He needed the freedom to be able to travel to exciting and remote locations. Together, they had swum with whales, camped for six months in the Dionisiades, canoed down the west coast of Scotland. It was on their year long African trip that Ella was conceived, with no hope of medical intervention.

It had been difficult for him to accept. He'd shocked her with his anger. He'd worried about money, their lack of a proper base, how his job was jeopardised, his wings clipped. She, meanwhile, had found somewhere to rent quietly in the hills above Inverness, letting him come and go, not wanting to pressure him. And instead of feeling alienated from the thing which grew inside her as she thought she would, she'd followed the progress of her little being with an intensity which surprised her. While Joe was travelling in the Peloponnese that winter, she was travelling through all stages of evolution from Silurian fish to crawling quadrupeds.

By the time Ella was born, Rachel was reading Wordsworth and Steiner and Ella grew up to believe that she had come from the stars, that she had chosen Rachel and Joe out of all the world's people and that she'd slid down a rainbow to Rachel, who had tucked her into her tummy, not far from her heart.

Joe travelled a lot when Ella was young, finding excuses to stay away – publishing deadlines, further research. But Rachel knew why, really. He was scared of commitment, scared of the one thing that had taken Rachel from him. He couldn't bear Ella's crying, the disturbed nights and smell of souring breast milk on the bedsheets. He hated Rachel's tiredness and her inability to concentrate when he needed her to. He hated her disinterest in sex. But gradually as the early days had eased into more regular routine, they'd won him back. Gradually he became interested in his little daughter, staying for longer periods, tentatively suggesting the summer Ella was three that they joined him on his trip through Romania. It was then that Rachel discovered she was pregnant again.

This time it was harder. She knew now that at just eight weeks dimples become ears and buds sprout limbs. She knew that by week nine there's a mouth with a tongue. She still refused counselling but dreamt then of tiny infants sluiced away through the drains of Aberdeen, running with blood.

She'd read that the Chinese whisper their secrets into holes in trees, sealing them in with mud. But today the soil is too frozen.

They reach home. Ella runs upstairs to a hot bath while Joe goes to kill the bird. He'd waited for their return. He knows she likes to pluck them warm.

Rachel had discovered the starring egg some months previously after the flock had rushed out in a scrum of feathers and ammonia racing for scraps. It was the peeping that had attracted her. There in the nest box was the one egg left to encourage the others to lay. Somehow, miraculously, it had stolen twenty-one days of heat from a multitude of feathered bellies. A little miracle. Ella was delighted. At last she would have a pet of her own. "My own rainbow baby," she'd pronounced confidently. For didn't everything come from the heavens?

They'd kept it carefully in the warming oven all day and by evening a fluffy ball of bright yellow down and beady eyes sat in Ella's hot little palm. Her Mirry. In the days that followed, she'd fed it oatmeal and chopped-up worm, kept it warm with a lamp, and let it sink down into her cupped hands and snooze.

It had been difficult to eat eggs after that. With each crack against the Pyrex bowl, Ella would protest, "But aren't we killing an unborn chick?" Joe would explain, in his scientific way, the ins and outs of fertilisation, how the egg wasn't really alive until the hen started incubating. Rachel would try to explain why they couldn't let *all* the eggs hatch. It was hard to understand, she knew. And Ella had known by the tender age of five that if you wanted to eat meat, you must be prepared to kill it. She also knew you named pets and didn't eat them.

One evening, Rachel had lifted the peeping chick from its cage and had taken it out into the cold night air. She'd placed it under the downy feathers of a broody, whose moist eggs were on the brink of hatch. And so Mirry had tricked her way into adoption. There were tears at first, but then Ella saw sense. Mirry had a mother to show her how to run after a moth or scratch under the currant bushes. It would have been difficult for Ella to teach her that.

Rachel realised soon enough that there would have to be a change in identity. She'd seen it as the tail feathers started to droop, in the gangly legs of youth and the yellowing eye. Luckily there were other youngsters to hide the deceit, the same black feathers, soft and thick. On the next "Where's Mirry?" it had been easy enough to fool her into thinking that one of the young hens was her own. Young cockerels meant meat.

Joe hands her the dead bird. Mirry's wings still flap a little, the toes still claw and grasp at escape but the deed is done. The sphincter muscles of the cloaca stretch and contract until finally the bird relaxes. A final scrabble of the feet startles before she tightens her grip.

She picks up the sharpened knife. Three perfect bronze circles squeeze handle against blade, holding it tight, in control. Her hand moulds easily around it, and for a moment she is comforted by its familiar feel. She brings it close to her face, closing her eyes, and inhales its faint smell which at first she cannot place but which gradually develops, as a print in a darkroom, into that of roasted nuts and myrtle, a warm steamy kitchen and . . . She opens her eyes, startled by the scent of a baby's nuzzling mole-soft skull, cradle-capped and pungent. She thinks of her dream of the night before, of the northern lights beaming down on her. She knows now that dreams are most vivid when the ego enters, when the embryo begins to grow, at just three weeks.

After she cuts off the head, it is easier. The eyes no longer stare from under half-closed lids. She knows that Amerindians only kill after looking their prey in the eye, that by this method they can tell which animals are ready for death and which not. She doesn't want to feel they've made a mistake. She's made too many. She begins plucking, pulling out the soft iridescent feathers by the handful. Yellow fat oozes. The skin feels so soft and warm and alive, the belly smooth and fleshy, the legs tight, sinuous. The feet, scaly and reptilian, trace their evolutionary line. The neck feathers are blood-stained, gelatinous and slippy, the skin underneath discoloured and loose like a scrotal sack. Rachel cuts it off, snipping it into tiny pieces to feed back to the flock.

Then the gutting. She shudders as always with the first raw slit, the first harsh stench of innards, of shit and blood, the egg-white connective tissue, clinging and giving. She imagines her own insides laid out like this on cold porcelain. Bracing herself, she sticks her hand into the cavity and gropes around in the warmth, pulling at the soft snaking intestines, the veined heart which spills out into the sink. She is relieved when two tiny testicles slip easily into her fingers, confirming her correct identification. It wasn't always easy to tell. She'd once tugged out a cluster of minute unformed yolks. Finally the crop and the crow, the chink of grain in the sink as the last supper spills. The washed cut oesophagus is like the neck of a new balloon waiting to be blown up and tied.

She cuts into the gully between smooth leg and fleshy breast. She joints then fries, the pieces sizzling in olive oil from Greece and cinnamon from Seychelles. Tears prick her eyes as she chops onions, swollen and weighty, ring upon ring cascading to the board. She's grown those herself. Then almonds from Italy, squeezing them from their hot soaking skins before adding all to the simmering chicken. The pure white of the kernels and the cinnamon scent soothes. It's growing dark outside. She sees the hens as they peck their way to bed across the freezing snow.

The smell of cooking stirs Joe and Ella from their corners. Ella comes running, she knows it's chicken tonight, her favourite. But Rachel keeps it from her, of course. Just as she will keep it from him. At least till she can no longer hide it.

WAITING
L. A. Hollywood

For real love
To heal the heart
Waiting
For real love
To do its thing
Waiting
For real love
To show its face
Waiting
For real love
To take the fear away
Waiting for real love to come and stay
Waiting.

A DAY BY THE SEA
June Munro

They were having a wonderful day. The school holidays had just begun and they were free for six glorious weeks. When they returned, they would be in the Upper Sixth Form and their days would be almost their own. True, everyone said they would need to keep up the level of work of the past year if they ever intended to go to college or university, but the girls knew they could get around the teachers they would have for the next year. Old Mr Armitage was always in a world of his own anyway. Mr Grimshaw knew that Julie was really interested in history so he was beginning to indulge her a little and let her get on with the periods she most liked to study. Mr Waddington certainly favoured Melanie. She was showing excellent ability in maths and he didn't seem to mind her helping Julie who was definitely not mathematically gifted.

They really only needed to be wary of Miss Moorhouse, the Senior Mistress and Principal Teacher of English. Miss Moorhouse missed nothing. Although kindly and able to inspire even the least appreciative of pupils by her readings of poetry or prose, she did the exact opposite of the male teachers. For pupils like Julie who showed real promise in her subject, her standards became higher and higher. Yes, they would have to look out for Miss Moorhouse.

They caught an early bus to Blackpool and by mid-morning alighted near the Central Pier and gazed at the panorama before them. The Tower gleamed in the sunlight with people at the top waving down to them looking like dots. The noise got louder as they walked towards the promenade and on impulse Julie said, "Let's go in and get our photos taken." The notice said two shillings for four.

"Let's split the cost," said Melanie and they drew the curtain and posed for a few moments, trying to look sophisticated and grown up. The photos took a few moments to process and as they examined them, an elderly lady approached with a toy poodle saying, "I'm going to get Suzie's photo taken. Is that machine any good?" Julie offered her the page of photos to see.

"Oh no," said the woman. "They are not good enough for Suzie," and walked off with Suzie in her arms. The girls looked at each other and collapsed into giggles.

"Did she mean that the dog has better taste or better looks than us?"

Heading towards the beach the girls sat down on one of the benches facing the sea. Blackpool had everything for entertainment that money could buy, but no-one with a modicum of sight could call it a beautiful place. The sands were dark and packed with people, donkeys, balls, ice-cream sellers while the distant sea looked brown and uninviting. Anxious not to crease their new gingham sundresses or disturb their beehive hairdos, Julie and Melanie decided to stay on the bench, soak up the sun and watch the world go by. The sea breezes were cooling as the blistering heat built up in the afternoon, but still they sat there. And what sights did they see! Overweight ladies waddling along in oversized frocks and cardigans, some more daring wearing shorts, or trousers and sun tops. Men sweltering in everyday trousers, shirts, even ties and jackets. Julie and Melanie had a field-day. Laughing and commenting wittily as the human sideshow passed by.

"Oh Lord, she looks like my Auntie Nellie," whispered Melanie as a thin lady who looked as though she had swallowed a glass of vinegar walked past with her equally thin and miserable-looking husband.

"Look out, here comes Jayne Mansfield," giggled Julie as a large lady with her bosom slung high enough to be a pair of earrings came into view.

The afternoon passed in a flash – what strange-looking folks they had seen that afternoon. Oddly enough, as the day wore on, the people passing by became more friendly, smiling and pointing to the girls with interest and not seeming to notice the derisive laughter directed at them.

"Look at that, the sights you see when you haven't got a gun," giggled Melanie as a gangly, spotty youth of about their own age appeared.

"Seen a mirror lately, girls?" he sneered and ambled on his way.

"Get him," giggled the two, but it was getting late now and they needed to eat before getting the bus home.

They felt a bit stiff, and their arms were a bit tender, but it wasn't until they sat down in the cafe and saw themselves in the mirror that the reasons for the smiles and the last comment from Spotty became clear. Staring out at them from the mirror were two of the reddest, most swollen faces they had ever seen, atop two lobster pink shapes in sundresses.

It's not easy to giggle when your face is burnt and the bus isn't the most comfortable place to be when your body is on fire.

Still, it had been a laugh!

STORM
Reg Holder

M r Robinson did not like his Captain. Unfortunate but true. From the first moment when he had joined as Chief Officer of the tanker, they had been at loggerheads. Maxie Smith a dour Aberdonian had come up 'through the hawse pipe', Robinson from a training ship and the two temperaments had clashed almost immediately. However the business of the ship had to continue and for the most part they were careful not to upset the equilibrium of her routine. Disharmony made for an unhappy ship as they well knew.

Robinson had joined in Trieste during the discharge and now the first loading in the Libyan terminal was completed. She carried a full cargo of crude oil for one of the refineries in the Delaware River. A winter crossing of the Atlantic lay ahead of them, a prospect that no one really looked forward to but accepted as part of their seafaring life.

The last of the mooring ropes let go and anchors heaved home, farewell was bid to the Pilot. He had been one of their own until recently and it had been good to catch up on the latest news and gossip.

At the last moment a message came to wait. Two drums of sample crude oil had to be delivered to the ship. Upset and angry the Captain paced the bridge wing; delays had to be accounted for and time cost money. Port formalities had to be gone through again as the drums were customs bonded and had to be delivered as cargo.

Finally the tanker set sail and Mr Robinson and his Captain had their first argument of the voyage. Maxie blamed him for not knowing about the drums and causing the delay. He was tired and ready for his bed for as Chief Mate he had slept only briefly while in port. Loading crude was a hazardous business and his job supervising the whole process meant no rest. The captain had taken his first drink of the day which added fuel to the flames.

Meanwhile deep in the Atlantic, the first stirrings of new birth whispered on a flat oily sea. Rippled wavelets danced along the underlying swell, glistening in the sunshine and creating small shadows on the water as they skipped over the surface. The sky, previously cloudless, now saw the first few wisps of high cirrus appearing before forming into long streaming tails.

Ominously those first faint stirrings were developing. The sea temperature warmed in response to the sun's rays, throwing moisture into the sky, condensing into huge clouds. The barometric pressure gradually fell and soon the storm system established itself with swirling winds increasing in strength by the hour.

'The Rock', guardian of the narrow straits, slipped past as the tanker left the Mediterranean, lifting into the Atlantic swell as she headed for the Delaware River and the refinery waiting for its precious cargo. Course was set to the North West on the directions of the Weather Routeing Service in Miami, thus departing from the usual southerly route to avoid the winter storms. These orders were followed against the instincts of her navigators, but the company was paying dollars for the service and good reason had to be given for disregarding their advice. However, all being well, their journey would be at an end in a matter of days and her crew could relax for a few hours before the next voyage, most probably down to Venezuela and back up to the States.

The storm ahead now developed into a full scale trough of low pressure, tightly packed isobars extending many miles to the south of Bermuda. It had been almost stationary to begin with, but now it lurched on an eastward passage, shaping up to become one of those storms that sailors feared the most.

The Captain came on to the bridge holding a telegram that had come through that morning. It was from the Routeing Service with the call to alter course further to the North West, lessening the distance that they had to travel but, unbelievably, ensuring that they would pass through the storm.

He went to the phone and summoned the Mate. The situation was not good and he needed to discuss their next course of action.

"Get south," Robinson said. "In my opinion we should never have listened to the Routeing Service; it's obvious that they are incompetent and now we are in a fix."

"What are you saying, Chief Mate? If you are blaming me then be careful." His ill temper only served to worsen a bad situation and the Mate fell into uneasy silence.

Moving into the chartroom, Maxie wrote on a signal pad and called to the Radio Officer. "Sparks," he said handing the message to him, "send this to those bastards in the weather service with a copy to head office."

"View latest instructions with concern. Indications are weather conditions worsening. Advise course be altered south."

The reply advised no alteration and the message from head office was that they were to adhere to the weather service route as far as possible, with the proviso that the safety of the ship lay with the Master.

"Fat lot of good that's doing us, Mate," muttered the Captain to his Chief Officer. "Bastards back ashore get their feet under a desk and forget what it's like to be on a ship. All they think of is money and those sods in Florida, only intent on cutting miles by sending us further North."

The next morning Robinson waited for the Captain to come to the bridge. He wondered how he would be, concerns mounting over his Captain and the bottle.

"Morning, Chief, how's your star sights this morning?" The Captain came through the chart room to the bridge. His eyes were rimmed red and the Mate looked at him anxiously.

"Sorry, Captain, could only manage one; we'll have to use it with the sun when we get the morning sight. Should get it but I don't like it for sure, no sir, not one little bit. We should get south as soon as possible."

"That's not good enough, Mate. If we don't get the sun we'll have to run on dead reckoning and we won't know where we are for some time."

Stung by the implied criticism the Mate replied, "We had a discussion about this yesterday, Captain, and I advised you then that we should ignore the routeing and get south. Now we have no option."

The trough continued on its inexorable path, spreading further south, deepening and filling the skies with an angry maelstrom of wind and scudding clouds. The sun rose, its angry red rays reflecting into the clouds, and back down to the steel grey sea. There was now no chance of escape for the ship. Water was crashing over the decks, the ship falling into the wave troughs, spume whipping off the crests. Gloomily the two surveyed the scene, tension between them hanging heavily in the air. They had been through many gales before. Indeed it was part of seagoing life and sometimes broke the monotony of a voyage, but this was one that they were not going to enjoy and it was not made any better by the bitterness between them.

"We had better slow down and ride this one out. Damn those people in Florida. What were they thinking of – routeing us right into its path. That's the last time I'll ever use them, whatever the company says."

Picking up the phone the Captain called the Chief Engineer, "Morning, Chief, we're in for a big one I'm afraid. We'll go down to half speed and see how she settles, and have your men on standby below. We won't see you back aft today that's for sure."

The day wore on, the wind reaching a crescendo and by now nearing hurricane force. The seas peaked ever higher, throwing huge walls of water over the deck and against the midships accommodation before swirling across the after deck. The beleaguered vessel heaved and rolled, plunging into ever deepening valleys of water, barely lifting before the next wall crashed down, the ship a tiny speck in a cacophony of sound and fury.

The journey down the catwalk was now impossible, effectively marooning the officers from their fellow crewmen aft and more importantly from food and sustenance. The pantry amidships only contained basic stocks of bread, milk, tea and a few tins of sardines. Her officers huddled on the bridge unwilling to leave throughout the day, finding support with each other. Rest called, though, and the night watches had to be kept. Reluctantly they went below leaving the Mate to his watch. The third mate returned to the bridge with a sandwich and a welcome mug of tea.

The dead hours arrived with a dull roaring in the centre castle space below – the sound of tons of water shifting equipment that had torn loose, racing from side to side and coming to a halt at the end of each roll with a sickening crash. Opening the bridge door, the second mate, now on watch, could just make out from the wing that the forward door to the centre castle was open; its clamps had come loose and it was swinging back and forth, each wave pouring tons of water into the space. One of the cargo tank lids had also torn free from its holding clamp, oil now spilling out on to the decks. Clearly something had to be done and quickly before the worst happened.

The Master returned to the bridge and a terse discussion with the Mate ensued – a decision had to be made. In the end the Master said, "There's nothing for it, Mate, we have to turn the ship and get that damn door shut somehow. God knows it's going to be dangerous enough and we'll only have a few minutes at best. Waves must be sixty feet at least. In all my time there's been nothing like it. God in heaven what did those Yanks think they were doing?"

A huge wave took the vessel further down, the weight of water below accentuating the roll with the whole side of the deck under green sea. As dark clouds scudded by, the moon suddenly shone through, ghostly and gone in a minute.

"Tell the Chief to batten every door down aft and get him to warn all those down there to be on their guard for a pooping." Turning to the Indian helmsman he said, "Listen carefully and when I give the order hold the wheel hard over, but come back easy when you have to. When we are round you must try to keep the ship steady with the waves on the port side."

"Aatcha Sahib, I'll do my best." Tension was palpable in the secunny's voice.

"Right, Mate, here goes and as soon as we are turned round you and the second get down quick and see what you can do. By the way keep a look out for those two drums of bonded crude. Ring full ahead and hard a starboard."

Slowly, agonisingly the ship climbed across the back of a wave, up and up and then fell wildly down the other side, her head burrowing into the water as she came round, beam-on first and then slowly her stern into the waves. The inevitable happened; tons of water cascaded over the poop on the port side into the accommodation, flooding the cabins. The propeller raced in the air as the stern lifted clear. Somehow the helmsman held the ship on course, skilfully turning the rudder to deal with the shifting seas.

Judging their moment the two officers raced down the ladders to see water pouring through the aft centre castle doors, crucially clearing the space with every roll. The sight that met them was hardly credible – long lengths of stiffened tank-cleaning hoses twisted and knotted like so much string, a spare pipe valve rolled relentlessly from side to side, paint drums lying ripped open. It was a scene of carnage. Timing his run, the second mate made it across to the door as it swung closed, frantically grabbing at the "dogs" and clamping them tight. The Mate spying at his feet, a large drum concertinaed flat, took hold without thought and threw it overboard, just as the Master arrived, swaying at the entrance. With tension at its height this was the last straw!

"Mate, you bloody fool," he shouted, "I told you that's cargo and has to be produced to Customs. There'll be no end of trouble." The argument raged back onto the bridge but now the most dangerous part was to come. The ship had to be put back head into wind and sea. How would she respond with the propeller and rudder clear of the water at times? Miraculously though, turn she did, coming round settling head into the seas with engine speed once again reduced.

Two days passed, the trough weakened and filled, wind and seas subsided, a watery sun peered through the cloud. Relations between the Master and Mate were now barely restored to speaking terms, lives had been risked and a flat drum should have been of no consequence. It was time to take stock and restore order.

The Serang appeared on the bridge, in his hands a flattened drum. "Sahib, this was found under the pipes by the pump room."

It was almost unbelievable. How could the drum have returned on board? And then to be found jammed under the cargo pipes was nothing short of miraculous!

Too late though to repair relations between the Captain and his Mate. The two would never sail together again.

REFLECTIONS
Carol Fenelon

For a Daughter

I am a watcher in the transient life
of my daughter.
Captured here upon the wall
I am immobile.
My eyes' caress is
impotent,
separate,
unfelt.
Her life has grown while I wait
in this half-shadow
reflecting her longings.
Flesh upon flesh will never come again.

To my Mother

She tries to guard me from her silent perspective
on my wall.
I finger her fleetingly,
a careful caress trailing the outline of a face
long forgotten.
I swallow slightly,
still having an intimate remembrance
of the way she ate across from me at table.
An occasional moment,
I do not seek her often now
having trained myself to forget.

ON SPENDING THE CHILDREN'S INHERITANCE
Valerie Weir

Now that we've retired we shall go away
travelling to exotic foreign parts
Tibet, Phuket, no common-place L.A.
for us. We'll be supporters of the arts,
buy up paintings to lend us some cachet.
Our marble floors will capture all your hearts
(installed by the designer of the day).
We'll spend and spend until good health departs.

The children will protest, *of course* they will.
"You're selfish, think of us," their shrill refrain,
"A care-home costs a fortune – it's unjust!"
"It's such as you describe exudes the chill
that spurs us on," we hasten to explain,
"to have it all, *before* we turn to dust."

FORBIDDEN FRUIT
Caroline Robinson

The filled forbidden fruit bowl was for show. Fingers that stretched towards it would be slapped back.

"Thems that doesn't ask, doesn't get." Mother said.

But we'd get when the skins had toughened to un-chewable leather, or the mandarins had indented to hexagons and held wizened, dried-up segments. Proffered soft bananas that looked like long, dark turds would be politely declined.

The wooden bowl smelt of sweet rot and housed decay, a thousand fruit flies, odd stray buttons and earwax-encrusted Kirby grips. It sat in the alcove above the meter cupboard in the living room. The alcove had been lined with a mini mosaic of purpley-pink mirrors. Some were cracked. The cat frenziedly chased and tried to kill reflections which on sunny days would waltz around the walls. The peach-emulsioned woodchip paper was all scratched and had bits missing.

Each morning, after breakfast we'd be dosed with a spoonful of cod liver oil which tasted nasty and a vitamin C tablet that we sucked on our way to school. It became mildly competitive to see who could get theirs to last the longest.

"Look, still got mine." A tongue would be poked out with the orange blob of evidence.

Tom Wood's garage had been the record distance, but I'd kind of cheated by secreting the pill in my duffle coat pocket and popping it back in my mouth again when we were way down the road and my brother wasn't looking.

One Friday, at harvest festival time, everyone took in cellophane-wrapped baskets of fruit to the school. I think they were for the hospital or the old folks' home, or maybe the teachers just ate them. You could never tell, and you daren't ask, in case they were for baby Jesus and it was something that you were supposed to know. We had a basket each – me and Bobby. So when we got down the road a bit, we went into the red phone box on the corner of Milton Crescent, peeled back the cellophane, undid the ribbons and each retrieved and ate a couple of satsumas and some grapes. The little baskets then looked a bit bare. We'd managed to peel the oranges in a oner, so we stuffed the empty skins with our well-used hankies and some rolled up pages we'd ripped out of the phone book, and sort of draped what was left of the twiggy bunch of grapes over the top. It was a bit awkward getting the Sellotape to re-stick and the recycled bow from Christmas time back in the right position but we thought we'd done a good enough taxidermy job.

The assembly hall had been decorated with flowers and loaves of bread made in the shape of squashed wheat sheaves that were propped up on high shelves amongst the cobwebs and bluebottle husks. The baskets were placed on an overburdened trestle table in front of the stage. Me and Bobby shoved ours down quickly, behind the lid of a big wicker hamper affair that had probably been brought in by Enid, whose mother drove her the few hundred yards to school and liked to show off.

Everyone took their places on the hard wooden seats. Two of the swots from primary seven handed out hymn books. We fidgeted silently as the teachers filed in and went up the stage steps and sat down on blue velvet-upholstered chairs, where they could survey us from above. Mr Beeton, the headmaster, stood at the rostrum in his brown shiny suit which was normally his Monday attire. Fridays were brown checked sports jacket with leather elbow patches.

I was pondering this deviation from his routine, when out from the newly installed loud speakers boomed, "Testing. Testing. One. Two. Three," followed by a high-pitched whistle.

"Good morning, children," he continued amidst the ear-splitting feedback.

"Good morning, Mr Beeton," we parroted back.

"Now children, today, on this special day, we have Reverend Philips to join us. I want you to welcome Reverend Philips."

"Good morning, Reverend Philips," we chorused like drugged robots.

Reverend Philips had long hair and played musical instruments which the grown-ups seemed to think was trendy. Us children regarded him with a quiet, unspoken suspicion, as one would a friendly policeman.

First we sang *All Things Bright and Beautiful*. Reverend Philips wanted us to clap our hands along with the music, which we did in a subdued, embarrassed sort of way. He strummed his guitar and Miss Watson banged out the notes on an out of tune piano, the foot pedals wheezing asthmatically. The teachers' voices drowned out the low mumblings from below. We were then supposed to close our eyes as the minister said a prayer. Chewing gum was retrieved from beneath seats; football cards were swopped.

A low *parrpp* noise came from near the stage. Even Mr Beeton's eyes were open. Leaning forward in his chair he scanned the front rows for the guilty miscreant. Just as the 'Amen' was being said it happened again, but much louder.

PARRPP.

Some of us had to stifle giggles behind praying hands. The headmaster was on his feet, eyes bulging, neck scarlet against his stiff, tight white collar.

The trestle table started to bow under its weight and with one loud creaking fart, collapsed.

Apples danced under chairs. Grapefruits hit the parquet flooring with a dull thud. As the little baskets rolled in ever decreasing circles a heavy pineapple rumbled up the aisle making a strange metallic noise. Everyone strained around to watch.

It came to rest at Steven Findlay's school bag. You could hear the clock ticking.

He stood up and shouted, "It's a bloody hand grenade."

Then chaos rained down. The Reverend Philips jumped off the stage and landed squish on a bunch of bananas. He pushed kids out of the way in his panic, and knocked off Billy Grimshaw's glasses. Billy had learning difficulties. Mrs Anderson became hysterical and was led away through the back stage door by the school secretary.

"Order! Order!" bellowed the headmaster.

"Fire drill." Leave slowly and quietly and assemble in the playground."

Someone then pressed the fire alarm button. The clanging bell was barely audible in the racket.

"My handbag? Where's my handbag?" Miss Watson's voice was heard whining above the din as she was propelled forward in the crush.

Hymn books lay trampled into trodden-on fruit; satchels discarded, chairs upturned.

Outside in the fresh air a slow drizzle misted down as we stood about in groups talking it over excitedly.

Mr Beeton appeared with the rest of the staff and ordered us into rows. A head count was made and checked and re-checked.

"Right, someone's missing. Who is it?" he asked the whole school as he marched along the lines, as if inspecting the troops.

"Who's missing?" he roared, spittle landing on Michael Pearson's forehead.

Silence.

Then, "Please Sir, Mandy had to go to the toilet," a tiny voice from the middle row said.

"Christ," he muttered under his breath.

Once we'd all been accounted for, we were told to go home.

"Have the rest of the day off. Come back on Monday."

We wanted to stay and watch, but weren't allowed to. The bomb disposal squad had to come down from Rosyth. Nearby houses and shops were evacuated. The road was cordoned off with black and yellow plastic stuff. It was on the telly. They retrieved a Second World War hand grenade that had been de-activated, probably by someone's Grandad, decades before.

MAN'S BEST FRIEND
Vivien Samet

He didn't like his childminder. He preferred outings with his dad. He was fed up with waiting in the rain. As the bus drew in, the boy decided to make a dash for freedom. He jumped on to the Citylink, his minder's stripey knitted glove still attached to his hand.

Remembering to duck as he sneaked past the driver-operated ticket machine he sat at the front of the bus in the outside seat of the pair reserved for elderly and disabled passengers. A golden Labrador sat next to him, at the feet of his master.

The boy looked down at the motionless dog, then up at his owner. He noticed the man's sunglasses and didn't think they teamed up with the thick knitted scarf and duffle coat. There was a bit of cream cake on his beard and the child looked down to see if the dog also had traces of cream cake on his face. Still there was no sign of movement. He started to stroke the Labrador's silky ears.

"Please would you not mind distracting ma dog? Can ye not see he's working?" the man barked. The dog's ears twitched.

"I thought the doggie was dead," the child replied.

"He isn't dead, nor is he asleep," the man continued. "He's counting the stops between Sauchiehall Street and the station." At that moment the bus stopped and the dog leapt up, guiding his owner down the steps and on to the pavement facing the station.

The boy jumped up to look out of the window. The light was beginning to fade, but he could just see them walking away together. He sat back and shut his eyes for a moment thinking hard until an idea came to him.

Perhaps, instead of a childminder, his dad could get him a guide dog.

DIRECTION
Sandra Bain

She was alone. The mountain was hers – not one other person within miles. The peace and solitude washed over her like a cool shower on a hot day. The mountain plateau spread out in a haze of mauve and above her the sky was a blue canopy stretching to meet the moorland.

Far below, the loch was a giant sapphire sparkling in a nest of green and brown. As the scene massaged her feelings the anxieties of the past months began to ebb.

She was herself – not Simon's wife, not Ron's mother, but a person in her own right. She wondered how she could ever have loved Simon, loved him enough to marry him. She had given him a son and it was around that time that she began to discover the real Simon. He was rich – perhaps that had attracted her – but he was also ruthless.

When they married he preferred that she did not work and that suited her. She had time to pursue her mountaineering activities. Then she became a mother. For a time she had combined the two – carrying baby Ron in a papoose as she trudged over the hills, but rock-climbing had to be curtailed. Then he became too heavy to carry, yet still too young to climb so she had to be content with low-level strolls.

Simon's success in business, she discovered, was at the expense of others. She could trace the birth of their problems to her sympathetic reaction to a colleague who lost his livelihood because of Simon's race to reach the top. At the time she had made her feelings very clear.

As tensions between them heightened she found some solace in bringing up her son but Simon could afford the most expensive – in her opinion not the best – education for their son. She still remembered the turmoil of that day when her little boy had gone off to boarding school. The renewed freedom to head for the mountains did little to fill the gap in her life and she lived for the occasional visiting day and the school holidays.

For years she had tried to convince herself that this was best for Ron. Deep down, she suspected that Simon wanted a clone – egocentric and callously ambitious like himself. She hated him all the more. Her trips to the mountains – the Alps, the Andes – became a welcome escape from him. She trained hard and her ultimate goal was Everest. Simon would raise no objections; being the husband of a woman who conquered the highest mountain in the world would enhance his reputation.

One of her dreams had been that Ron would develop a love of the mountains too. For a time fulfilment had looked promising but his initial enthusiasm had died and he latched on to the aimless existence of a bad crowd. His decline in fitness raised the suspicion of substance abuse although he vehemently denied involvement.

She lay back on the warm heather and watched a plane track its way east. Three hundred souls were travelling there thousands of metres above her, heading for a destination. They would have purpose. She knew the twinge of envy was irrational. She might be suffering, but how could she know there were no suffering souls on board that plane? No one knows what is going on in the lives of strangers.

Heaviness settled on her, breaking the spell of the mountain. She began to relive an interminable flight from Switzerland. With two companions and a guide she had reached the top of the Matterhorn. It had been spine-tingling. She had experienced such joy and had wanted to share it with the world . . .

There was a message waiting for her at the hotel, to phone Simon. There was news about Ron.

Poor woman, what had she done to deserve a son like that? She knew what they had been saying. Her fears that Ron was into drugs were confirmed. She had never suspected that he had been involved in several muggings to feed his habit. Now he had been arrested. She blamed Simon and his pretentiousness which had sent the boy away to school. Simon blamed her for spending too much time on the mountains and leaving Ron to his own devices. That was the final curtain on their relationship.

She was shocked when Ron was shut away for eight years for attempted murder; it almost sent her adrift but she felt a certain satisfaction in seeing the blow to Simon's ego. He didn't care about his son, only the damage to his own reputation.

Simon's hardness of heart was what gave her some cause for relief; he would not be visiting the Young Offenders' Institution so she would never have to suffer meeting up with him. He would not even be thinking ahead to the time when Ron would be released into a world ready to pounce and lure him back into his habit. But she would. She had plans for building up a new relationship with her son. It would be hard and painful work but she could make the effort.

But for today she was alone. She was not Ron's mother; she was a mountaineer. She was a woman who in a few days would be on a flight heading east. All the arrangements were complete. Simon would never boast about being the *ex*-husband of the latest woman to conquer Everest.

Your reason and your passion are the rudder and the sails of your seafaring soul. The quotation came unbidden but seemed apt as she contemplated the ebb and flow of her life so far.

PARK SHELTER
L. A. Hollywood

Cliff goes into one of the park shelters and sits on a bench. Two lovers run past holding hands, laughing, just happy to be with each other running for the bus.

He slips off one of his shoes, then with an old penknife, cuts a thick piece of cardboard to cover the split in its sole. Then he puts the shoe back on, stomps and reties the lace. As he puts the knife away, the light rain blows over and a rainbow appears above the allotments, next to the park. Betty, the bag lady, comes into the park, shoes held together with string and parcel tape, tea-cosy on her head, greasy grey-brown hair hanging around her face and her old fur coat hiding stained clothes. Betty mumbles to herself as she drags along an old shopping trolley full of things left over from a church jumble sale. Mothers call young ones to them, telling them not to look at her. Betty goes past. A bunch of kids out playing football laugh at her, people walking dogs move out of her way.

Cliff follows Betty out of the park to the Day Care Centre for their one hot meal of the day, thinking, "A kind word from you to her might make all the difference. Are we teaching the young to be too hard too soon?"

IDEAL HOME
Carol Fenelon

I can straighten the pictures
on the wall,
nice neat lines,
reflections of my life in
monochrome or colour,
smiling and unsmiling
back at me.
I can straighten the cups
in the kitchen,
small neat teapot,
plate ready for meal for one,
fridge full of female food,
salads, yoghurt and
carefully chilled wine.

I can have this life if I want it.
Carefully controlled,
not quite antiseptic,
but no frayed edges,
no unwanted stories.
My bed is neat and tidy,
pillows straight,
duvet pulled into order,
tucked in at the edges,
forced into submission,
virginal, cool,
smooth and safe,
ever so safe.

But my neat tidy bed
is a double and
I have ensured a space for you.
I like my rumpled weekends,
I like the way your body fits
into mine while I sleep.
This clean space in the week
has become less inviting,
and I have started to not sleep
without you.

My cups and plates,
knives and forks are starting
to look at me in serried rows,
two by two,
not one by one.
My fridge boasts evidence
of your stay,
curry and beer
while a shirt lies ready
to be washed,
tangled in my female fancies.
I hold it to my face
to breathe it in and savour you,
suddenly wanting you.
This ideal home isn't quite so ideal now,
without you.

THE CROOKED JADES
Susan Szymborski

The Crooked Jades is a fascinating band and last night I was treated to a fascinating gig. The concert took place in the Seallam! Centre in Northton, Harris. This choice of venue was an organisational masterstroke for many reasons.

Not only did it show the festival's forward looking commitment to take music to as wide an audience as possible, it also gave visitors the chance to discover some of the most beautiful landscapes the islands and, indeed Scotland, has to offer. The trip will stay with me forever: soaring mountains, turquoise seas and stunning beaches.

This remote part of the Hebrides also proved to be a fitting context for The Crooked Jades. The American five-piece (who feature on the *Oh Brother Where Art Thou* soundtrack) describe themselves as 'old-time revivalists'. Replete with wiry beards and thick rimmed glasses, they play a range of instruments from fiddles to banjos in the style of rural American music rooted in the 1900's. Against the backdrop of Southern Harris, it felt like the band were coming face to face with some of the traditions they so fervently laud. As one local surmised, "They certainly fit in here with their flat tweed caps!"

That said, their old-time has a modern edge. The Crooked Jades' affinity with this style comes from a rejection of bland commercial music and the things it stands for. They choose, instead, to 'see the beauty of difference'. This is manifest in their off-kilter rhythms, flattened, sliding notes, odd lyrics and the initial adjective of the group's name. Their unusual mix of old and new is most starkly evident in the slick-suited frontman who stands in contrast to his folksy-clad band mates.

With songs about rural life, slavery and migration, the venue itself provided another interesting link between this American folk act and the small Western Isles enclave. The recently opened Seallam! Centre displays genealogical information about the long-standing history of emigration between the west coast of Scotland and America, Canada, New Zealand and Australia. The extensive set consisted of a mix of barn-dance romps and poignant, innovative ballads. The bluesy *Goodbye Trouble, The Soul of Man* was a stand-out track and a firm favourite with the crowd.

Indeed, although the small audience was initially uncertain about what to make of this quirky act, a strong, appreciative bond formed between the two camps over the course of the night. A bond, which given the brilliant match of music, values and venue, seemed wholly inevitable. A captivating performance of Heb Celt Fest 2006.

*The following story was inspired by a
postcard sent from Spain by a member of Ross-shire Writers.*

FLAMENCO
Valerie Weir

The thrum of guitars vibrates through the courtyard and thrills
Annunciata to the core of her being. Pedro Soler has come from
Córdoba to visit his people – Pedro Soler, the greatest flamenco singer
in all Andalucia, even in all of Spain. Annunciata listens to the
rumours about his drinking; about how he must be high on drugs to
sing the way he does. Everyone knows, they say, that the greatest
flamenco singers are tormented souls. She listens but she doesn't
believe a word.

"Ignorant peasants," she thinks, "what they don't know they make
up." Annunciata, although she hasn't been to the city yet herself,
knows better.

So! They are holding a fiesta in Pedro Soler's honour. His mother
and grandmother and all the older women are indoors preparing food
for later. The courtyard is alive with colour from the bougainvillaea
tumbling over the roof, the pelargoniums cascading from their pots on
the walls, to the blues, greens, yellows and reds of the girls' dancing
dresses.

Everyone is clapping and watching Immaculada and Lorenzo
dance; everyone, that is, except Annunciata. She is looking at Felipe.
Felipe has taken his hat off. Without it, he looks younger, vulnerable.
Annunciata thinks the broad-brimmed black hats lend height, maturity
and mystique to the men. She has known Felipe for ever and they have
been betrothed for as long as she can remember. They grew up
together and she knows that together they dance the best flamenco in
the village, perhaps the best in Andalucia. She looks at him, trying to
catch his eye but he fixes his gaze on the couple in the middle of the
crowd. He's being deliberately annoying. Annunciata wants to convey
to him with her haughty look that Immaculada and Lorenzo are as
nothing. For them Pedro Soler is singing only the *cante chico* – a light

and cheerful air. She wants to say that that is the only flamenco the pair are capable of dancing – mere froth! For her and Felipe, Pedro Soler will sing the *cante jondo*.

At last, she and Felipe take the floor. In their dance they interpret Pedro's song. It is in the holding and letting go: in the angular postures of Felipe's strong arms and legs, in the sinuous curving of Annunciata's delicate arms, in the thrusting and yielding, in the turning of her dress to allow the frills and folds to arrange themselves just so, in the retreating and advancing, in the glance of sparkling eye to sparkling eye.

Through it all, the sad ululation of Pedro Soler's magnificent voice rises above the roof tiles. He sings the deep song of the oppression of his people: the invading Visigoths, the Romans and the Moors; he sings of bitter romance, of lost love, of hardship, grinding poverty and death.

The guitarists' hands blur as the notes leap and resonate. The *duende*, the spirit, possesses the dancers as the bright chords resound off the hard sunlight. Pedro's voice soars and catches. For the finale, the primitive drumming stacatto of their feet pounds the floor of the courtyard, beating and beating all that sung darkness into the earth. They are both in tears when they stop.

Then somehow Pedro is holding Annunciata's hot fingers. She tilts her chin to acknowledge the deserved applause. Pedro Soler bows and gestures to include Felipe. Applause doubles and thunders.

People shout, linking their names, "Annunciata! Felipe!" There is whistling and delighted laughter. With a final salute and before anyone realises what is happening, Pedro Soler turns and runs from the courtyard with Annunciata in tow.

In the following days, although Felipe knows and is assured by his family and indeed the whole village, that he danced the greatest flamenco in living memory, he is inconsolable in his loss.

"Annunciata," he weeps, "Annunciata!"

THE LONG ISLAND
Christina Macdonald

The mail boat set sail on the stroke of midnight, just as the Sabbath ended. Angus was standing at the stern of the boat looking down into the black water dancing with reflections from the pier lights. The engines began to rumble into life and shouts from the quay followed as the mooring ropes were hauled from the bollards and the boat was set free. Watching all this activity, Angus thought it was symbolic of his own life, letting go of the ropes which had bound him so securely to his home and family: the churning water below echoing his churning thoughts of all that had happened in his life up till now and all that lay ahead . . .

"Perhaps when you lot at the back have stopped talking, we might be able to continue with the lesson," Mr McAndrew spat out. "The island which we have the privilege to inhabit lies 58 degrees North and 6 degrees West. In fact, if you look at the map on the wall, you will see that we are almost on a par with Moscow and Labrador."

Angus gazed gloomily through the classroom window at the trees in full leaf and wished he was elsewhere. Anywhere else would be good, anywhere but this stuffy second floor classroom where the sash windows were stuck fast with fresh paint on a hot Friday afternoon just before end of term.

He longed to be out on the shore, pacing the rippling sand still damp with the receding tide, picking up the pink shells tiny as a baby's fingernail or treading gingerly on bunches of greenish-brown seaweed by the rock pools. Pools of clear purity cradled in the rocky shelves where he could bend down and scoop up small creatures or drop in stones to disturb the calm surface.

"MacLeod! Day-dreaming as usual. Answer my question!"

"What question?" Angus thought in rising dismay. He had often been on the sharp end of the teacher's tongue, too often for comfort. One of these days there would be a letter of complaint sent home to his mother, or worse, a confrontation on Parents' Night. All his faults and misdemeanours would be set out before her to contemplate with her customary embarrassment. He was not aware at the time, but these evenings churned up all her feelings of guilt and inadequacy as a single parent.

He remembered the time in the Primary School when he had written his diary in his school exercise book. She had been dismayed to see that he had told his teacher that "Mam sold our front room carpet for £26." She had been mortified and furious that he had divulged this private event. "What will Miss Mackay think of us, making us look as if we are hard up?" she had shouted at him when she came home, tears in her eyes.

Angus had never forgotten that moment. He had learned to play his cards closer to his chest after that, both in school and out. As he grew older he began to understand his mother's fierce pride, became part of it, absorbed it into himself.

"Well, Macleod, I asked you to repeat the exact position, latitude and longitude, of the island of Lewis." Angus looked at the shiny blackboard. He had forgotten to bring his glasses with him and try as he might he couldn't make out the writing. He was afraid to admit his inadequacy. "Come out here!" shouted McAndrew and lifting the lid of his high desk he took out the infamous three-tongued Lochgelly. "Hold out both hands crossed," he bellowed. A sharp pain shot up Angus's arm and he looked at the reddening palms. Struggling to keep tears at bay, he turned on his heel and sat down quietly at his desk. By now his ears were burning. His class-mates looked on in rebellious silence. They too had known the sharp sting of the belt and were afraid to show solidarity at this moment with their fellow sufferer. Sympathy would come later when they were outside in the playground.

McAndrew had a big problem. He had returned from the war, battle-scarred – not physically, but in a more sinister way, mentally. Many a confrontation between pupil and teacher occurred in the classroom. Pieces of chalk, blackboard dusters went flying to the back of the room, but no-one dared to speak up or complain to anyone in authority. After all, he was second-in-command in the school.

Angus recalled the day when McAndrew had checked them all for talking and said, "Hands up those who want the belt?" A forest of hands shot up. "Now hands up those who prefer to do lines?" Angus opted for the lines. He hated physical confrontation. That night he had gone to his bedroom and looked up his favourite poem, *Elegy in a Country Churchyard*. It had enough lines to qualify as a punishment so he wrote it out in his best handwriting. Next morning, on the bell, McAndrew called the pupils to his desk. Quite a queue of writers had formed on one side and on the other were the future victims of the strap. Angus was at the front of the queue and handed over his offering, rather proud of its appearance. McAndrew snatched it and ripping it in pieces, hurled it into the cane wastepaper basket. All the other scribes had their efforts mangled in similar style. Then McAndrew belted them all and told the other side to go home and write a hundred lines. A smile of pure masochism lit up his face. No-one said a word. His rule was absolute.

When Angus reached the croft house in the afternoon, he found his mother out at the back pulling peats from the stack. The stack was getting pretty low but the peats he and his uncle John had cut out on the moor in the spring would soon be ready to be brought home. He had cycled out several times to the peat bank and turned the little stooks so that all the peat would be exposed to the drying winds. He remembered times in the early spring when his father used to take him out with him, cutting the slabs of peat for Angus to grab and throw on to the heather bank. He recalled the squelchy sensation when his fingers sank into the dark brown slabs.

He remembered the plague of midges every summer, driving them crazy by the loch, and the day he helped his father to fill the sacks with the dry peats to take them to the roadside for the lorry. This potato sack was packed tight. His father stood up from the peat bank and struggling, hoisted the sack on his slight shoulders. There was a hole in the bottom of the sack and all the peats had fallen out. Angus had collapsed laughing in the heather. His father had laughed too, but in embarrassment that he had not checked all the sacks before loading them on the handlebars of his bicycle.

The laughing had died that summer. His father was no longer around to cut and stack and harvest Nature's providence. He'd died suddenly of a heart attack at forty-two when Angus was only eleven years old; his two sisters were in Primary school and his brother Johnny still in the pram.

The day of his father's funeral, he and the others had been put to stay at a neighbour's. His father's coffin had been carried from the house the short distance to the graveyard by a posse of sombre-clad men from the village. Angus had seen none of it. Children did not go to funerals then, but he had often seen similar processions. The dignified way in which the mourners proceeded in two straight lines behind the coffin and then in turn taking the weight of it for a few paces before peeling away like a sober strip-the-willow in slow motion letting others take up the burden.

Angus had grown up rather quickly after that. His mother needed all the help he could give. They had no close relatives on the island now apart from his Uncle Johnnie, though neighbours were kind and caring.

Soon now he would be away to University on the mainland. He was pre-occupied with his exams and his concentration was bombarded daily with the temptations of the outside world: walking along the shore, exploring the woods, fishing for cuddies off the end of the quay with the other boys. The long northern June nights when darkness never fell were restless times for all, especially the young.

All through the summer he worked away at his Languages. He'd won a small bursary to Aberdeen University so that would help, and his grandmother had put by a bit of money for him when the time came. The autumn nights began to draw in. Then, on the first of October, the day had come to leave the island.

The tide was high and it had been a struggle to climb up the steep gang-plank with his large trunk in the lashing wind and rain. A rough crossing was on the cards. He had looked down over the rail for the last time and waved to the retreating figures of his mother and uncle . . .

The boat lurched as it made its way out of the safe harbour into the open sea. Angus, jolted back to the present, stood looking back at the receding lights of the town. To the right he could just see the cemetery where his father lay. Once out of the sheltered harbour, a stiff wind whipped up the waves. The welcoming sentinel of the lighthouse slowly faded into the darkness and they were out in the open sea. Angus stood in the lea of the deck and pulled his jacket tight. The faint glow of a cigarette revealed the presence of a dark figure nearby, elbows on the rail. He recognised one of his class-mates.

"Hey, cove," he greeted Angus, gripping the rail as the ship began to roll. "Off to Uni then?"

"Yes," replied Angus tightly, though trying to sound casual. "What about yourself, Donnie?"

"I'm off to join a ship down south. Going into the Merchant Navy, same as my father and my uncle. It's good to be free though, isn't it! The great wide world out there waiting for us!"

He paused.

They both fell silent as they watched the old familiar life of the island vanishing behind in the wake.

THE WORTHLESSNESS
Henriette A.O. Stewart

I am the worthlessness. Confidence is my opponent; unhappiness is my friend. Last night you felt me so passionately, I decided it's time I introduced myself properly.

I have evolved through times, feeding on pathetic fears, turning them to my advantage. It takes time, you know; fears can be both obvious and obscure, but I like a challenge. To make the happiest person fall into a deep depression is to me a victory. I am the one, who makes you compare yourself to others, makes you think that the grass is greener on the other side. When you look at yourself in the mirror, I will draw your eyes towards your self-proclaimed imperfections, and magnify them. I whisper in your ear that you are worthless, useless, ridiculous and stupid.

I have your full attention now. By all means stick your fingers in your ears and sing "la-la-la-la-la-la" at the top of your voice; in fighting me, you are acknowledging my possession of you, and now that I have introduced myself you will never get completely rid of me.

Of course there will be times where you'll almost forget me. You can scarcely believe you once felt so worthless you almost wanted to kill yourself. That's when I'll strike again, for I was with you all along. I will plunge in and wound your self-assurance, strangle your cheerfulness and cloud any sunny disposition. Then I'll feed you misgivings and pessimisms; in fact, I gave you some just this morning when you were waking up. They were nasty weren't they? Made especially for you.

So you want to talk to me now? Argue with me? Good, you're putting up a fight. It's boring when someone gives up easily. I like you; you amuse me. Will I use you? Absolutely. You will be my delightful little pawn, as you go about your day – sulking, jabbing snide remarks, exuding negativity, building up resentment till you eventually blow your top and hurt your nearest and dearest. And I have a knack of making you feel everything is, in the end, your own fault.

But I'm coming on too strong now. Your sighs have become groans and your eyes shun the daylight. You sleep all day and spend your waking hours in a stupor. I want to keep you alive, so I will pull away for a while. I'll go and inspect my other pawns and keep confidence in check.

Aah look . . . here comes a little ray of hope already.

RETIRED LIBRARIAN'S TALK TO
THE WORTHING WOMEN'S INSTITUTE
Vivien Samet

Good evening, ladies, and thank you for inviting me to talk about my career with the library service which, amazingly, spanned a period of almost five decades.

Can you hear me at the back? Good, I am pleased you have installed a loop-system since my last talk.

My library training started in 1953; in fact I am still using my pair of coronation mug bookends. Of course in the pre-computer age things were very different, though personally I found old shoe-boxes a highly efficient filing system. Not only library tickets were stored in them – one morning I inadvertently discovered the head librarian's ham sandwich and a banana and hastily replaced the lid of her file. Now everything is far too streamlined.

My entire library career was spent in Worthing public library – not because I wasn't adventurous. In fact I went trekking in Peru one year and accompanied a party of American librarians to Antarctica another time. I am currently planning a bungee jump from the Eiffel Tower to raise funds towards helping our partially-sighted readers.

What I liked about Worthing was the pace – residents mostly made up of retired people, not to mention that I was on a trolley bus route – essential for a non car owner. Only very recently did I buy a car, open top, with personalised number plates . . . and there's a story: I cannot tell you how many times Terry Parker was sent a reminder for overdue books – meanwhile his fines were accruing and reaching astronomical heights until finally he returned with sixteen books. I knew he had just completed community service for some minor offence, but he was always friendly and an avid reader, which was to be encouraged, so I waived his fine and it wasn't until Terry had left the library and I was putting his books back on the shelves that his lottery ticket fell out.

Anyway, back to my career in the library and to tell you some of the many reasons I was eventually awarded an O.B.E. for my services. Frankly I thought it might have come sooner and it certainly aroused more than a whiff of jealousy among other public libraries from as far as Brighton and Kensington. They even offered sweeteners for my contract to be transferred – well, a box of *After Eight*s – but I wouldn't take bribes.

In my day I was considered very modern, and fought long and hard for crèche facilities, somewhere for parents to be placed under supervision while kiddies could run riot. I have always placed freedom very highly.

Another innovation I was responsible for, though sadly it failed to catch on in other libraries, but proved to be of tremendous help to the vertically challenged who found difficulty in reading titles of books on the top shelves, and that was to fasten my old pair of opera glasses on an elastic, thus putting their problem in focus as it were. Next to them was a Swiss cow-bell for anyone to ring for assistance should interest go beyond the title. Another example of how one person's initiative can help others' lives.

I do like a story with a neat ending and when the time came for me to accept my O.B.E. at Buckingham Palace I found it fitting for me to have travelled alongside the Queen as it were, with her career beginning in the same year as mine.

The great legacy of my library career has been the many subjects I have learnt through books, so when I finally retired I was fortunate to be able to fall back on the many skills acquired through the reading of such books as 'Teach Yourself to be a Ventriloquist', 'Learn to Tango in Ten Days', and 'Ninety nine ways with a baked potato'.

This isn't the last chapter of my story as I still hope to pass my driving test – after twenty-nine attempts. The video didn't provide adequate tuition, nor the many self-help books. However, I got friendly with a retired driving instructor who was always coming in to borrow gardening books, especially ones on hybrid roses; he and I go out for a drive most Saturdays.

Meantime, my sports car with the personalised number plates remains parked outside my semi, thanks to Terry's lottery ticket. I was glad to waive his fine.

As they say: 'If you cast your bread upon the waters it comes back buttered toast'.

Thank you, and goodnight ladies.

EACH SIDE OF THE DOOR
L. A. Hollywood

They stand each side of the doorway
Ten feet tall, arms outstretched,
Looking to the heavens.

Once they were saints
Calling the faithful to church.
No longer called Luke and John,
Now they're just
Rock and Roll.

No more bells on Sunday morning.
Instead of ministers
It's a DJ and disco
That flashes
Seven nights a week,
Sound and light
Calling their faithful.

WORK
Jim Piper

"Well Mr . . . er?"

"The Great Hondario. That's my working name. My real name is John Jones."

"I am Dr Roseanburge. Dr Geddes has referred you to me but has not forwarded any notes. Now I understand, Mr Jones, that you were in an accident."

"Yes, six months ago and the psychologist at the local hospital recommended that I come to see you, doctor, as you deal with accident claims – specifically psychological ones."

"Yes, that is correct. Now what exactly is your problem?"

"In a nutshell, if you'll pardon the pun, doc, I got run over in Covent Garden where I work, by a cycle courier and hit my head on the pavement. I was unconscious for half an hour. When I came to I had been struck normal."

"Pardon, Mr Jones?"

"Struck normal."

"What do you mean by 'struck normal'?"

"Well, doctor, I am an avant-garde performer. I have always made people laugh, right from the age of two. Now I am, according to the local psychiatric hospital, as normal as they can define with their tests."

"Right, and you want me to fight your case in court?" The doctor sighed. "You know I have never refused or lost a case."

He got up and walked over to the furthest filing cabinet, opened it, and with his back to The Great Hondario appeared to pour and down in one, a very large whisky. Returning to the desk, he looked hard at his client.

"Mr Jones, this is most definitely the oddest case I have known in my twenty-five years of practice."

"You see, doctor, my whole life has changed since the accident. I don't get invited to parties any more because I am no fun. Yesterday I spent two hours choosing a new grey button-up cardigan."

The doctor pulled his jacket closed. (He, himself, wore cardigans).

"You see, doc, I ain't ever been anything like normal. Last year I ran the London Marathon backwards in a lady's dress reciting Edward Lear's poems while playing the fiddle, and all for charity."

"Hm, Mr Jones."

The doctor looked longingly towards the filing cabinet but the thought of being struck off and losing an income of sixty pounds plus, an hour, steadied his nerves.

"Being normal is not really considered an affliction Mr Jones. Out there are millions of normal people."

"Yes, doc, but many of them rely on me for entertainment."

The doctor pulled his desk drawer open halfway. The Great Hondario could just see a bottle of pills marked 'emergency use only'. This seemed to reassure the doctor, though only just.

"Doc, I am losing a thousand pounds a week. In the summer in Covent Garden tourists go wild at my antics but I just can't do them any more. My work as an entertainer has been ruined. Why last night I read 'Saga Magazine' from cover to cover and even cut out interesting articles which I stuck into a scrap book. Then I decorated an empty jam jar to make a pen holder."

"That is perfectly normal, Mr Jones."

The doctor hurried to the filing cabinet and downed a good treble then returning, sank back in his seat.

"Look, Mr Jones, I am going to refer you to a friend of mine."

"Why do you all keep sending me to someone else? Do you only know how to make people normal or what? You see, doc, you must admit I have been changed by the accident. Last night I had cocoa in a reclining armchair and recorded 'News Night' so I could watch it again. Usually I would have been getting someone's party going or have been in the pub standing on my head drinking a pint of beer. I've got thousands of free pints doing that or playing requests on the piano with my nose – pick the tune, if you'll pardon the pun again."

The doctor's eyes rolled around in his head. He did some deep breathing.

"Come back in a week's time, Mr Jones. Meanwhile I shall do some research."

After reading 'The Readers Digest' in the waiting room, The Great Hondario left.

Later that day he found himself being addressed by a nurse.

"Mr Jones, are you feeling better now?"

"Why am I in hospital?"

"You were in an accident."

"Whose grey cardigan is that next to my bed? Why is my head bandaged up?"

"Oh here comes WPC Munro who will explain things more clearly."

"Hello, Mr Jones. Are you feeling up to making a statement?"

"Well I think so. What happened to me?"

"All I can say at the moment is that you were walking down Harley Street when an empty whisky bottle was thrown out of a second storey window and hit you on the head knocking you out."

"Whose brown suede shoes are these?"

"You had rather a lucky escape as it happens, Mr Jones."

"What do you mean?"

"Well, straight afterwards an eminent psychiatrist jumped out of the same window narrowly missing you."

"Oh?"

"Yes he's in another ward. We can't get any sense out of him. He just keeps going on about 'normal'. What's wrong with being normal? Do you want to bring any charges against him, Mr Jones?"

"Call me The Great Hondario and as for charges, I'm cured. The man's a genius. I've been to ten doctors who all failed me. He's done the trick! I'm mad again!"

"Why do I always get the mad ones?" thought WPC Munro.

Then The Great Hondario asked her if she'd fancy going to a party that night. She told him to calm down, but after a moment's thought asked him where the party was.

"I don't know. I'll just start one," he replied and grabbing her hat

he put it on and danced around the ward shouting,
   "I'm cured, CURED. Yes! Party on!"

Six months later, a bill board in London informed the public:-

NOW APPEARING AT A LONDON THEATRE
THE AMAZING NEW COMEDY DOUBLE ACT
THE GREAT HONDARIO AND CRAZY DOCTOR
SUPPORTED BY
GLAMOROUS WPC LILLIE MUNRO

MAKING SENSE OF IT ALL
L. A. Hollywood

Rivers of steam run down cracked windows. Two figures – wrapped in rugs, fingers entwined, palms locked together – lie in a fishing hut off the beaten track, trying to make sense of it all.

Wind howling, rain, ice-tipped branches brush against roof and sides, the river runs in spate over rocks, waves splash against banks.

Dying lights from scented candles stuck in cut-down beer cans, flicker around the room, their lights casting shadows, adding to the loneliness of their time together.

Branches twist and break, some floating away with the river, others lying around the hut. They dream on without a thought of the harsh moonlight breaking in on their world.

Unheard By Them

Something screeches in pain lost out to a hunter of the night. On silent wings it glides following the river's tree-covered banks as it twists, trends away from the hut.

Wind dies, doors rattle, ice covers windows. Snow falls casting a scene of unwanted beauty, leaving them with a sense of loss.

Candles flicker away, the room now full of mixed senses, stale air. Cold moonlight breaks its hold on them as time and reality come again without warning.

Last embrace. Unwinding near-dead fingers while watching snow flakes drift out of sight through smear-stained windows. Like words unspoken, thoughts unsaid. Until next time.

FIG IN JAR
Heather Macleod

This is my sarcophagus.
In hot glass I lie
like parts of something mummified
amber flesh spilling
these scarab seeds, unbroken.

You go to throw away.
But wait.

Unclip the lid.

Nose in to the transmutation,
the honey-scented song, intoxication,
the essence of those hot rock-straddling limbs,
taut skin concealing secret, folded flowering.

Imbibe that perfect plucking hour when,
splayed in summer-swelling heat
and carmine as desire,
the hidden blooms,
discrete, unscented,
distil a dew,
new, unfermented,
and then

be tempted.

Take, eat.

I purge the body, cure the skin,
satisfy the whim of every man.
This is my promise.

Take heed.

For shaded in these strangling folds
are prophets, traitors, gods of old.
And knowledge.
But note.
There is no sweetness without stain.
There is no prudence without pain.

A tree is known by its fruit.
So wait for the ripening.
The buddha enlightening.
Half-ripe, I'm poison.

ON THE SPUR OF THE MOMENT
Catriona Tawse

"That net curtain could do with a wash," thought Chrisanne peeping through the scullery window to look out for the town service bus when it came round the corner of the hill past Norrie's garage. This always gave her time to do up the buttons of her shabby tweed coat and knot her head-square tightly below her chin. Chrisanne checked that her purse was in the big shopping bag before closing and locking the front door. There were glimpses of sun among the scudding clouds and larks sang their praises high in the sky. The scent of newly cut grass filled the air; Kenny Grant had the mower going behind the hardy Fergie tractor whose peeling grey paintwork and dented mudguards bore witness to many years' service.

With a brief blink of its orange indicator the bus slowed towards her and stopped, letting the door hiss open.

"Good morning Mistress MacIntyre," Donnie Diesel greeted her from behind the steering wheel. "Nice day isn't it. And how are you today?"

"Yes it's a grand day indeed. I'm fine thanks. How's yourself these days?"

"Can't complain really. The back still gives me bother off and on. You'll be away up the town then?"

"Just that, Donnie, a wee parcel to post." This insignificant information was better offered, rather than prised from her question by question. She took her ticket and her change and sat down. There were few passengers; she recognised no-one other than Trawler Dan nodding off in a seat near the back. After a lifetime at the fishing he liked to go to the Mission for the crack with the other old worthies.

Far to the left the rippling sea glistened. As the bus rattled its way along the single track road Chrisanne looked out at the blue expanse and wondered how long it would be before they could have that promised trip to the mainland. Her sister in Inverness kept an open invitation to visit. If only her husband wasn't so tied to his work, and so reluctant to be away from home. Chrisanne sighed. She felt as though life was passing her by with her fortieth birthday only weeks away. Sheep grazed nonchalantly right up to the narrow grass verges and bolder ones lay down on the tarred surface as if it was provided for their comfort. Amused by this rural idiosyncrasy summer visitors stopped to take photos but lorry drivers on their way to the ferry blasted air horns and directed expletives at unperturbed fleecy backs.

There was the usual mid-morning queue in the Post Office. Two 'Position Closed' signs were up behind the protective glass. Chrisanne's turn eventually came. The parcel was weighed and exclaimed over.

"Oh Australia is it? A long way to go indeed." Catriona Mhòr at the counter was just about as nosy as Donnie Diesel on the bus.

"Yes," offered Chrisanne. "It's to my niece for her fifteenth birthday. A Fair Isle cardigan, I knitted it myself."

"Oh isn't that grand, she will be pleased, just the thing for the cold weather," Catriona went on in her homely way attaching the required stamps with great precision. Chrisanne nodded and smiled to people in the line as she made her way to the exit.

Turning along South Street she noticed that there was a bit of a stir in front of what used to be the Hydro Board showroom. It had stood empty for several months following relocation to the edge-of-town retail park and speculation as to its new occupancy had been rife. Suggestions had included pet shop, computer sales, furniture store or yet another Estate Agents. Others with long-faced pessimism predicted the infiltration of betting shops or one of these modern places selling unmentionable things to the depraved and immoral.

Chrisanne crossed the street for a better look. Above the façade an artistically lettered sign proclaimed, "Head to Toe . . . Fashion and Beauty." In the wide window the modishly clad mannequins in elaborately posed positions were almost obscured by posters and banners and little coloured flags.

"GRAND OPENING !! Special Offers This Week Only!! Complete make-over!! Be the first!! Buy One Get One Free!! Don't be shy, Ladies, COME ON IN!!" And rather to her surprise Chrisanne took the spur of the moment decision to do just that.

The interior was a welcoming haven of subdued lighting and mystic perfume. She saw soft seating, low tables with magazines and brochures and pale pink walls displaying photos of elegantly coiffed heads. Alongside, various framed certificates declared the expertise and achievement of the workers therein. Soothing music oozed from invisible speakers. The whole relaxed atmosphere was designed to lure the undecided to a different world far from household chores and family obligations. Chrisanne allowed herself to be led through by a smiling young assistant attired in a pink nylon smock above sleek black velvet trousers.

For Chrisanne the next few hours drifted past in blissful tranquillity. Her unruly hair was shampooed and styled and streaked with blond highlights. She had her first ever leg wax. Her feet were massaged and manipulated and her hands deftly manicured, though Chrisanne had some doubts about the deep blue nail colour. Her face had been cleansed and toned and made up in a way that even she agreed took years off her. Thinking it would be a shame not to complete the new look with some decent clothes Chrisanne had once more offered up her seldom-used credit card and signed for a smart navy three quarter length linen-look jacket along with a neat skirt in a toning shade of blue. It had small pleats front and back and was a whole lot shorter than she was in the way of wearing. The frill-necked beige blouse would "go with anything" the sales assistant had promised. Her new shoes had a modest heel as Chrisanne felt some attention should be paid to the practicalities of rural life.

She boarded the bus on Port Street carrying the cast off clothing in the big bag. Donnie Diesel's face was a picture.

"Great heavens, Mistress MacIntyre, I hardly knew a bit of you," he laughed. "Wait till your husband sees you, he'll think he has a new woman." Chrisanne took her seat, tugging ineffectually at the skirt which scarcely covered her knees. She was aware of the waft from the heady perfume she had sprayed on at the last minute and was relieved when they reached her road end.

In the house opposite Peggy Macsween was setting the table for tea.

"Would you come and look at this," she called to her sister Dollag in the kitchen. "Some painted hussy is away up to the MacIntyres'. She's got a huge bag of something with her." Dollag came through, nodding her head sagely.

"She'll be in trouble of some sort, mark my words. Chrisanne will soon put her right."

Chrisanne, back in her own kitchen, was guiltily realising that there was not enough time to prepare and cook the liver and bacon casserole she had mentioned to her husband before he left for Rhynagol that morning. He'd be back any minute now and would have to make do with quiche and salad instead. She heard the car coming up the gravel road as she was putting water in the kettle.

The Reverend Iain Bàn MacIntyre climbed thankfully from his old Orion, pondering sadly on the lack of moral fibre of the young couple at whose marriage he had officiated and at the same time anticipating eagerly the tasty supper which awaited. He laid his black hat and his well-used Bible on the hall table and went through to greet his wife . . .

PHOTO
L. A. Hollywood

Old photo cracked around the edges
covered with cling film
looking out of place, out of time
black and white, faded brown.
Picture of a family
all gone their separate ways
lost in the haze
of drinking and drifting,
losing out on life.
Friends, family, the list shorter
with each passing year,
each drink you took,
each doss house you stayed in.
Roads no longer hold a wonder for you
like they did,
cold nights in bus shelters or railway stations
thumbing lifts just to see where the road ends.
A million miles gone under foot.
You followed roads around the world
to places new. Now they have gone.

You sit under this tree in the old folks' home
watching the shadows from the sun,
waiting for your last ride.

Still looking at an old photo.

MOVING ON
Caroline Robinson

I packed the boxes and labelled them clearly. I'd even devised a code to cause less confusion and time-wasting: an 'S' for me – Serena, a 'J' for James, my husband. If the label was written with red ink the contents were destined for the living room of the new house, green for the kitchen. Hopefully, by sticking to my carefully crafted instructions, the removal men would place each carton in the correct room.

Having whittled down my accumulation of possessions to four stout boxes, I expected the same downsizing from J. But he dithered moon-faced over his congestion of Dinky toys and flicked through back copies of *Model Railway* magazines into the small hours. I'd feign sleep when he came to bed with the fusty scent of his past clinging to him.

I managed to stuff bin bags with his forgotten clothes: garish kipper ties adorned with naked women, their nipples cherry-red and pert. I'd sneaked old rugby boots and crackly-with-static nylon shirts into charity shops, their stained armpits an embarrassment.

On the week of the move James seemed smaller, greyer somehow. He bid me to travel on ahead, muttering about cancelling the milk and the security of empty houses.

I arrived ahead of Pickfords. The journey a joy, being bright and everything shining with newness, flew past backwards. I even cast my old headscarf out of the train window. A suited man, sitting opposite, coughed disapprovingly and raised and ruffled his *Financial Times* as a barrier. I laughed, something that sounded strange – half remembered and forgotten to my ears.

The house seemed bigger being unencumbered with things. I echoed through rooms, pulling windows open – letting the sweet air and birdsong in from the forest. Going outside I gathered fallen twigs and fir cones; using my skirt as a carrier, I held the hem high, and noticed the lorry bumping up the track. I turned my back, but blushed knowing the men had seen my knickers. Suddenly, feeling alone and isolated with their arrival, I went back inside and shook my skirt into the empty hearth and straightened the material.

They came carrying a box each and placed them on the hall tiles. I didn't have the composure to remind them of my instructions – the coloured code. They carried in another box and the older of the two produced a paper and pen from the pocket of his overalls and asked me to sign it.

"The rest. Where's the rest of the stuff?" I asked.

"Four boxes for Mill Den. That's the lot." He looked at a spot over my left shoulder and coughed in the same way the man on the train had done and pushed the yellow biro a few inches nearer.

DEAD GUITAR
L. A. Hollywood

Corner of a block of flats
Green bin lid held up by
The head of a dead guitar.
Keys lost, broken strings
Wrapped around its neck
Empty cans supporting the body.
Once fine mother-of-pearl patterns
Ripped away from its front,
Hundreds of phone numbers
Faded with time from when
You travelled the world.
No more plucking rock and roll
Or blues to the beat of drums.
Bin emptied, your last ride
Is to the dump, abandoned
Without fuss or fame,
You're out of time in
An electronic era.

SNAKE
Heather MacLeod

And so she began:

He was born during a night of storms. Rain had lashed down on the tin roof of the mission hospital, lightning had wrenched her apart, she'd groaned with thunder. The frangipani trees outside her window had been shredded, in a hiss of tearing leaves, their sweet blossoms swept away. They drowned now in a sea of red mud, which only the day before had puffed up like ashes with each slow step she took towards the maternity unit, her dress hanging heavy against her taut stomach, her nausea increasing.

And finally it was all over. Or all beginning. The end of one life, the start of another, two others. For she'd not only given birth to a baby, she had been born a mother. She hadn't expected it to be such a painful process, the emergence into a new world, the shedding of old skin. The snake had achieved it with such perfection. She saw everything in a bright fresh light, as if even her eyes had been sloughed, and each sense sharpened to a point. Around her room her few possessions lay discarded like dry and brittle scales. She smelt her blood, the yellow ooze of her tender seeping breasts, felt her baby's mole-soft head with its pungent odour. That night she had crossed an invisible boundary, the storm her ancient rite of passage. And deep within her now grew the presence she'd felt so often in the forest at Ngulu and seen in the ngambe's eyes, the primeval force that somehow would bind her and her baby together forever.

It all started with the snake. Before that there had been the visits to the 'ngambe', the medicine man to ascertain the cause of her problem. She'd answered questions about her physical condition, her diet and dreams, her duty to her ancestors. Cowries had been thrown, water poured, the movements and patterns of ripples and shells had been interpreted. She'd been given a bitter concoction to drink, a poultice of green herbs for her belly. A chicken had exchanged hands in payment, a tub of honey. She was always fascinated by the rituals; she loved the dark, smoky interior of the ngambe's hut, thatch blackened with the tar of endless fires and hanging with the mysterious objects of his divination – feathers, bones, a monkey's paw, ancient calabash spoons to weigh and measure. And in an enclosure, a spider, possessed of extraordinary wisdom, black and hairy which shuffled the dust, dug deep holes and was thus in touch with the underworld. Its stylised figure appeared everywhere, on the carved wooden poles outside his hut, on his finger ring and the carved buffalo horn from which he drank white mimbo. There was something other worldly about the old man too. Mediating between the human and spirit worlds, he was part of something she was not. She gazed into his deep dark eyes, as he crouched, loin-clothed, before the ashes and felt she could drown.

But at the back of her mind she still doubted. She was dogged by the unbelief rooted in her scientific background and Iain's gentle cynicism. Facts and figures, logic and analysis still influenced her though here in this African village, of diviners, witches and warriors, she felt them being nudged to one side. Instinct and intuition coupled with a primitive fatalism were nestling closer. The rulers of Benanga, the Chief and his elders, seemed to possess an innate understanding of things, passed down from generation to generation. They could explain the need for the forest as a life-giver, not in ecological terms but with ancient stories of gods and spirits, sacred and evil. She loved the feelings these tales evoked in her, the sheer vertigo of their heights, the horrors of their depths. They stirred in her something atavistic. These people knew the pain of the forest's death without being lectured by a pair of ecology graduates. They also knew its demise lay outwith their control, pressures introduced from afar. "Green missionaries," Iain had jokingly called them when they were posted to this remote outback, whose dwindling forests were home to wildlife the conservation world was crying out to save. But she wondered who would be the ones to listen to the sermon.

The handling of her inability to fall pregnant had been a prime example of her doubts and reshufflings. While Iain's practical mind came up with biological explanations and hospital check ups, she had thought of the witch doctor. Though, of course, they'd do the hospital

125

first. There, her insides were wracked open, spotlighted, searched with latexed fingers. She had felt vulnerable and exposed, a physiological problem to tease out and explain. At home, Iain had mapped her cycle like the moon, plotted her fullness, mounted her like an experiment. Only when that was all over, dried and dusted, had she pursued her own course. After her visit to the ngambe, an altogether different experience, she'd decided that would be that. She would shrug her shoulders and accept the inevitable. The problem with white people, she thought, was that they always opposed fate to the last ditch. Or tried too damn hard to explain it logically.

On the day of the snake's arrival, you could have cut the air with a knife. The hot breath of the Harmattan had arrived, charged with fine desert sand. An insidious film of red dust wafted over the vivid new growth. It was as if the gods had decreed Africa, in all her verdant nakedness, was too tempting to view and must be veiled like a bride before her rebirth in rain.

She sat hulling maize cobs on the veranda, kicking dry husks into the big ditch surrounding their house. It was the noise that alerted her, of maize husks rasping like withered leaves in a soft breeze. She looked up longing to feel a breath of wind but instead glimpsed a sinuous flow, slowly writhing through her morning's work. In and out it wove until the movement ceased just below her right foot which hung over the gutter's edge. Then the slim head of a snake appeared as slowly, deliberately, it raised itself from gutter to veranda in one sleek slide. It passed so close to her poised foot she could almost feel the ripple of its muscles. Then it halted by her stool. She was frozen in fear, knowing the terrible energies of a snake's poison, realising that sudden movement could prove fatal. For a few breathless moments they stared at each other, its cold unwinking eyes piercing her own, its beautiful olive green head, redolent of power and death, swaying curiously. Its tongue flickered, in and out, tasting her scent, smelling her fear. And then slowly, gracefully, it retraced its steps and was away, silently slipping across the red earth in front of the house.

She let out a shuddering sigh of relief, wiping her clammy hands on her thin dress, and watched the snake's passage down the track, like

126

a ripple of wind-blown sand. And she was suddenly overcome with a terrible desire to follow it. She had a limited knowledge of snakes, enough for her to realise that this was a forest snake, its thin head and long body designed for tree life. So why was it here in the village?

It wasn't until she reached the boundary of Ngulu, the sacred forest, that she had the crazy notion that perhaps the snake had intended her to follow. Though she had lost sight of it way back she had followed its faint marks in the soil. Even when she lost track of those, she felt drawn to this patch of forbidden forest. There was nothing she could do but enter.

At once she was in cool delicious shadow. The sun which had blazed down in all its tropical fury, was suddenly and deliciously gone, filtered and split by the thick green canopy. She scrunched through the deep crisp carpet of leaves, straying further and further into the depths. She'd been in the forest many times before, spent months living rough, studying birds, bats, frogs, those indicators of life's changes, but she had never come here, never to Ngulu. She closed her eyes and breathed in the forest's scent – the scent of decay, that damp fungoid odour. She inhaled the deadness of leaves, fallen wood, flowers, animals, everything that ever lived and died, bored and churned by a vast factory of a billion tiny mouths, turned to a vast rotting womb sucked ceaselessly by new growth. She absorbed the sounds – the muted screech of a cicada, the incessant tonking of a distant bird, the soft rustle of leaves, gyrating gently to earth. She saw the waltz of a butterfly, a trickle of creamy latex oozing from wounded bark, the fat body of a beetle. She felt that every corner was filled with life, delicate, beautiful, strangling, poisonous. It watched her every movement. And she felt something else, something she'd not noticed before. Though she could not touch or see it, she knew it was there, like the force which exists between magnet and iron. She felt that without it everything would disintegrate and explode into infinity.

She heard the pool before she saw it. Parting spiders' webs, skirting bamboo, she came to it softly. Beautifully illuminated in a shaft of sunlight, it lay cradled between two great mossy cliffs, separated by an enormous sloping rock. Gently this great flat mossy slab tilted towards the pool like a giant's slide, and down it, crystal clear, sparkling with sunbeams, slipped water, in soft weaving currents. These arrived almost noiselessly at the pool's surface sending out not a seething mass of bubbles as in a waterfall, but a gentle rhythmic wave. On the cliff above, a huge tree grew, its massive bole spiralling up seeking light, its branches dripping heavily with epiphytic growth. Its great orange red roots writhed along the cliff edge, one descending down, until its vineous growth, coiling over itself, tumbled into the pool below. She laughed aloud, gasping at the beauty of the place, unleashing in her mind the Norse myth of Yggdrasill, whose roots were nourished by three wells of purity, wisdom and poison. But which was this? Without a doubt or a care in the world she sank to her knees in thick damp moss and drank deeply of the cool water. It was only when she raised her head did she see the snake, gliding noiselessly away on a sun dappled branch.

"Where have you been?" Iain asked.

"To the well at the world's end, where I promised to marry a snake!" She laughed, and hissed at him. But in the morning it was no laughing matter. A branch of nkeng lay in the compound, a summons. No women were allowed in Ngulu, she had transgressed traditional law. She went humbly before the village elders begging the Chief's forgiveness, carrying cola nuts in an effort to appease. She was told she had polluted Ngulu. Ritual specialists would have to cleanse it at great expense. But then she was white and ignorant, what could be expected? Her forgiveness bore a price – two chickens, a goat and four calabashes of palm wine. Iain rolled his eyes at the news. Masa, how could she have been so stupid, and now a big party at their expense! But it was the snake, she said, hearing the folly of her words and in the cold light of reason, doubting her inner self.

It was when she knew for sure she was pregnant that the snake came again. This time they both saw it, forewarned by hens, which flew wildly and noisily away from the lithe form in a maelstrom of feathers and dust. It came as before, tasted, stared and left, lost amongst the undergrowth before Iain could find his shoes and follow.

Over the weeks, they often saw it around the compound, gliding noiselessly through the hibiscus, coiled at the base of the kibongolingos tree. Once, in undergrowth around the compound, she'd nearly stepped on it, as it feasted on the struggling, hissing body of a chameleon. But it wasn't until the snake strayed into the tree nursery that the decision was made to kill it. It was slinking in and out of half-grown seedlings, hugging pots of forest trees that would be planted with the rains. The nursery workers held an instinctive fear of snakes, and chameleons, sweeping the paths and yard bare of life, all the better to spy out reptilian movement. So it came as no surprise that they wanted to kill it before it bit them. This, of course, was the practical solution. Its visits, though interesting, were becoming a dangerous nuisance.

Yet she was uneasy. In her mind, she pieced together the events like half-remembered Greek myths. Had she not been led to the sacred forest by a serpent? Had she not now fallen pregnant as if by a snake? Iain laughed at her skewed logic. Secretly she prayed that the visits would end. At night, she dreamed watery dreams, of swimming with serpents in crystal clear water, of giving birth to a child half reptile half man. She would wake, restless, soaked in sweat.

Her prayers were answered by the ngambe man. He knew of her trespass in Ngulu and on hearing of the snake's continuing visitations, had entered the spirit world, dressed in feathers, anointed with the red dye of camwood. He had returned with the news that the snake was no ordinary one; it was the spirit of Mnkong Moteh, father of the forest, founder of the Benanga tribe. It must not be harmed. It was coming to give her its blessing.

Tracing figures in ashes with a charred bone, he told her the tale. How long, long ago, when the land was clothed in thick forest, Mnkong Moteh had led his people to this place from the sand-blasted lands to the north. He brought nothing with him except a drinking cup in which he held the water of life. With this he had blessed the forest, and from it had sprung the pool in Ngulu. Mnkong Moteh was a strong man, a good and noble leader, a fine hunter who loved and respected the forest life. He learned to possess the power of change and could transform himself into any animal. He clothed himself in leopard pelts and the red feathers of forest birds. On his deathbed, he made his chief advisors promise to bury him in the forest, not in the palace as tradition decreed. But after his death they went against his wish – how could they bury such a noble leader in the bush? The day after his funeral, his grave was found open and from it, traced in the dust, wisped the trail of a snake. They followed this trail to Ngulu and where it ended they found, coiled round a tree branch, the olive green form of a serpent.

With the ngambe's interpretation of events, she was given permission to go to Ngulu whenever she wished. Each time she went she felt the same invisible force that she'd felt on her first visit, a presence she couldn't describe. And though she searched the top of the cliffs, she could find no stream filling the pool. Water surfaced as if from the underworld to pour down the slide. And though the pool seemed to have no outlet, it was always icy and crystal clear.

The last time she saw the snake was towards the end of the dry season. She felt heavy, swollen, her belly ached. She'd scrambled laboriously to the forest's edge and stood now in the coolness, longing to splash water on her drum tight skin. But an angry hiss made her hold back. In dappled shadow by the pool's edge was her snake, writhing. There was a pain in its eyes she hadn't seen before. It took a while before she realised it was shedding its skin, writhing and rubbing against the grey green rock. In its anxiety to rid itself of its cracked and useless clothing, it had torn its delicate newness. Beadlike dots of blood stained its bright fresh scales, the scent attracting the curiosity of a passing ant. She sensed its vulnerability, felt its fear of being eaten alive by tiny carnivores. She backed away into the darkness, leaving it to complete its metamorphosis in peace, secretly wishing that she, too, could rip her own taut skin and bring relief by sloughing against the boughs.

That night, as the first drops of rain met the high closed canopy of the forest, her labour started. She finally found relief, not in Ngulu, but in the mission hospital. Her ears had rung with the ululations of visitors, the Chief's wives, who, cowrie-crowned with rattles shaking, had brought the baby's name. She'd related it down the telephone to her anxious mother. "*What* are you calling him?" she asked incredulously.

"Mnkong Moteh," she'd replied.

"And is that the end of the story?"

"Almost," she said, "except everyone expected you to be born black and have no eyelids! Oh, and you were born in the Chinese Year of the Snake, if that doesn't confuse things." He laughed, turning over the well-fingered treasures in the box – the red feather of a turaco, a seed necklace, the crudely carved figure of a man. He made the blueness of a Venetian bead shine through his fingernail. Finally his fingers came to rest on the perfect translucent skin of a snake. "Now it's time for you to have all these." She pushed the open box gently towards him and it puffed closed. A waft of Africa billowed out, smoke-tainted, blackened, mysterious. He breathed in deeply as she lay back into her pillows, and sighed.

THE PLANT LOVER
June Munro

I loved it when I bought it
And I placed it in the room.
I sat back and I waited,
And I waited for a bloom.

I moved it to the sunroom,
And I moved it to the hall,
I moved it to the kitchen,
But it didn't bloom at all.

I talked to it, I sang to it,
I told it funny tales,
But the buds stayed firmly closed
And then the leaves began to pale.

I watered it, I sprayed it,
But it died and went all brown.
So I'll buy a Flora Plastica
When next I go to town.

THE CONTRIBUTORS

Sandra Bain worked as a teacher in Perthshire and Peru over a period of nine years before returning to her roots in the Black Isle. She has had several non-fiction articles published in magazines and has researched and written the history of Tore School – *Growing for the Future* – which was published in 2005.

Carol Fenelon has been writing fiction since participating in a WEA class five years ago. She wrote professionally as part of her employment for many years but has taken the leap over into fiction and thoroughly enjoys the challenge. She is a published poet and is now working on a collection of short stories.

Reg Holder was born in Kenya and raised in Uganda, coming to the UK to join a training ship before sailing on cargo ships and tankers. He is a Master Mariner and spent the greater part of his life after leaving the sea working in the Middle East. There he wrote a weekly golf article for the *Gulf Times*. Nine years ago he followed his parents to settle with wife, Pat, in Ross-shire, where he has a marine consultancy and continues to work here and abroad. Otherwise he plays golf and enjoys his writing with the Ross-shire Writers.

Leonard A. Hollywood (Writer) is a member of Ross shire Writers group.

Jackie Liuba lives among the mountains on the West Coast, within inches of the sea. She works in a Walled Garden, writes stories for children, as well as for herself, and has just completed an Open University Creative Writing course.

Christina Macdonald (Hill) was born and brought up on the Island of Lewis. She has been involved in writing in various genres all her adult life and has had articles and letters published in local newspapers and a Christmas story published in *The Ross-shire Journal*. In 2005 she gained first place in her category in the Age Concern Scotland competition.

Heather Macleod is an ecologist, full-time mother of four and organic gardener. When she can, she scribbles and wishes there was more time to do so. Her work has been published in various places including BBC Wildlife Magazine and on Radio Scotland.

June Munro has Highland roots and is married to a Lairg man. Having lived in the North of England until 2000 they moved to Ross-shire, where they now live at the tropical end of the Struie. She has travelled widely and is a dedicated people watcher. After a career in various branches of nursing and raising two sons and a daughter she now has time to enjoy her love of reading, writing and indulging her grandchildren. Some of her pieces have been published in women's magazines.

Jim Piper lives near Strathpeffer. He enjoys humorous creative writing, water colour painting and walking in the countryside as well as watching sunsets and the night sky. One of his poems has been published in *The Ross-shire Journal*.

Caroline Robinson lives in Dundonnell in Wester Ross. She writes stories at night with the curtains shut so no one sees. Some of her short pieces have been published in Scotland and America. She and her partner are building their own eco house.

Vivien Samet is originally from Brighton, Sussex, but moved to Scotland in 1970. A photographer by profession, she began creative writing five years ago. She has attended writing courses at Moniack Mhor, Kiltarlity and a poetry course in Venice.

Henriette Stewart was born and grew up in Denmark but has lived in Scotland for sixteen years. She started writing four years ago when she joined a creative writing class (later Ross shire Writers). These are her first published stories.

Susan Szymborski recently returned to her home town of Evanton after studying English Language at Glasgow University. She hopes to train as a journalist and won a BBC Radio Scotland competition to be a reviewer at the Hebridean Celtic Music Festival 2006.

Catriona (MacRitchie) Tawse was brought up in Achiltibuie, educated at Dingwall Academy and trained as a teacher in Aberdeen. For many years she lived in the Turriff area and recently moved to Strathpeffer where she became involved in writing, painting and learning Gaelic. She loves music and visiting Skye.

Valerie Weir is a Lowland Scot who has lived in the Highlands for twenty-seven years. She is interested in global environmental issues. An avid reader she chooses not to have a television. Now that she is retired, the organic garden she has been making for fifteen years is at last progressing. Retirement has also given her time to take up writing. She was highly commended for a story in the 2004 Highlands and Islands Short Story Association's inaugural competition. Some of her poetry is written in Scots.